TRANSFORMATIONS

READINGS IN
Evolution,
Hominids,
and the
Environment
FOURTH EDITION

Edited by
Dianne Smith, Ph.D.
Santa Rosa Junior College

We travel together, passengers on a little space-ship,
 dependent on its vulnerable resources of air, water, and soil…
preserved from annihilation only by the care, the work
 and the love we give our fragile craft.

Adlai E. Stevenson (1900-1965)

 **Custom Publishing**

Boston Burr Ridge, IL Dubuque, IA New York
San Francisco St. Louis Bangkok Bogotá Caracas Kuala Lumpur
Lisbon London Madrid Mexico City Milan Montreal New Delhi
Santiago Seoul Singapore Sydney Taipei Toronto

TRANSFORMATIONS

Readings in Evolution, Hominids, and the Environment

McGraw-Hill's Custom Publishing consists of products that are produced from camera-ready copy. Peer review, class testing, and accuracy are primarily the responsibility of the author(s).

1 2 3 4 5 6 7 8 9 0   QSR   QSR   0 9 8 7 6

ISBN-13: 978-0-07-338673-7
ISBN-10: 0-07-338673-1

Editor: Mike Hemmer
Production Editor: Nina Meyer
Cover Design: Maggie Lytle
Printer/Binder: Quebecor World

Transformations
Readings in Evolution, Hominids, and the Environment

Introduction

Anthropology and an environmental perspective are inseparable. Human life, indeed our very appearance was transformed by the specific environments in which we evolved; today our biological needs and cultural habits are transforming all our global environments. This complex web of transformation cannot be fully explained in a simple reader like this, but the issues and experiences presented here will broaden the reader's exploration of the inseparable transformations that describe the evolution of humanity.

Most individuals think of their family tree as kin they see at holidays and family reunions or the ancestors they can describe with personal names or categories. But each person has a family tree that is much larger than an individual kinship list and it needs only one name: *hominid. Hominid* describes *all human beings and a few pre-humans* as well. It is our *scientific* family name.

Most anthropologists call the earliest of all hominids *Australopithecines.* You and I today are known as *Homo sapiens* or modern humans. Together and with many groups in between, we hominids span about four million years on earth. The environmental anthropologist instantly sees important similarities and difference between the earliest and most recent hominids. Through this book and this class, the reader will begin to recognize these features as well. Here are a few points to get us started.

What do modern humans share in common with early humanlike beings or the *Australopithecines*? We both walk upright on our hind limbs; we have larger brains than other animals; our opposable thumbs allow us to manipulate our material world with strength and finesse; and we depend heavily on our sense of sight to make our way in the habitat. Even though *Australopithecines* were quite small beings...some adults were not quite four feet in height and had smaller brains than we do today...we share all general hominid features and they are ancient kin in the span of human time.

Most anthropologists would agree that we had *culture* throughout our hominid family past as well. *Culture* describes the *behavior and traditions that are learned and shared within social groups.* Significant similarities and differences in learned behavior should be explored between our first ancestors and ourselves just as we explore our similar and varying biological appearance. Why? Because both culture and biology have been important means of adaptation in our relationship to the environment.

Throughout our past, biological and cultural change...*hominid evolution*...took place as we struggled to extract food from wild sources in our environment and rear our young safely. Our earliest traceable ancestors appear to have occupied forests or semi-forested areas as our contemporary primate cousins or apes and most monkeys do today. Nature favored those hominid ancestors that became stable, two legged walkers on the ground, had larger brains, and more agile hands. Their genes were passed on to their young. We were transformed and became more efficient hunters and gatherers of wild plants and animals. We created tools, weapons, and traditions that would enhance our survival and build our numbers on earth far beyond all other close animal relatives. Our biological changes were linked with greater cultural transformations and a few millions of years later, we no longer gathered our food from wild sources, we had learned how to grow it and raise it in nearby fields and pens. Throughout the course of about four million years, our bodies developed their current appearance and our cultures became very complex systems. Our hominid population dominates life on the planet.

Remarkably, in the larger span of life on earth, our time here is brief. Yet it is a powerful and complicated era that deserves great attention and study at a holistic level. We have become large brained and intelligent beings and we no longer extract small elements from our environment to survive biologically. Through our changed biological appearance and our expanded cultural traditions, we use the environment in ways that can and do deplete the very life sources we depend upon for biological survival. We now live in a time of enormous challenge and dilemma.

Unraveling human/environmental problems is not an easy task and it cannot be achieved in a single college course. Don't feel frustrated however, as solutions are underway and so is your study of them. Through anthropology and environmental studies one can begin to see the complex web of human life, culture, and nature on earth. Arriving at fresh conclusions and solutions to the environmental dilemmas we face will take time and deliberation. In this text, the reader will accumulate insights from evolutionary theory, genetics, race, disease, anatomy, the study of our cousins--the monkeys and apes, and fossils. These are the pieces of the puzzle that anthropologists know make an important picture of human life on earth. They are also keys to use when attempting to resolve environmental problems. It is up to us to study each of these parts and put this picture in clearer focus. When anthropology and the environment are studied together, the potential for new understanding can be transforming.

**TRANSFORMATIONS: READINGS IN EVOLUTION, HOMINIDS,
AND THE ENVIRONMENT**
Edited by Dianne Smith, Ph.D.
Santa Rosa Junior College
Fall 2006

Introduction

Table of Contents

Feder, Kenneth L.
"Epistemology: How You Know What You Know."

Humans observe and assess both their local and global environments with keen eyes and large brains. The human brain records such complex information, we may need to re-evaluate what we have come to think of as "true." How can we be sure we're seeing our world objectively? What value does a scientific point of view bring to what we "see" and need to understand?

Oliwenstein, Lori
"Dr. Darwin"

The next great medical advance may well be the application of Darwin's theory of natural selection to the understanding of human disease. The human body is an environment where natural selection and evolution takes place. Darwinian medicine searches for insight in this struggle between disease and survival.

Hsn, Honor
"Bittersweet Harvest: The Debate Over Genetically Modified Crops."

There appears to be little collaboration or shared testing of genetically modified (GM) crops between scientists and environmentalists. Are we going to regret not taking opportunities to feed starving populations more easily and without as many crop pesticides by using GM foods? Or, would we risk setting forth on a genetic journey unlike any other...one that could lead to irreparable environmental damage with GM crops?

Race is a culturally created concept that continues to be misused by many as a biological or "scientific" one. Race indeed exists, but only as a learned and shared set of beliefs about the meaning of superficial biological differences.

Section II - Primate Anatomy and Behavior

With hominid adaptation to terrestrial environments, assistance for mothers in childbirth becomes essential. Culture and biology interact for successful natural selection.

Tracking gorillas in their natural habitat includes many challenges for primatologists but also yields keen, firsthand insights into their natural behavior and their vulnerability to poachers. Both theoretical and active conservation should be evaluated to preserve them.

Survival of our closest relative the chimpanzee depends on complex social and cultural learning between mothers and their infants. Without the skills a chimp mother teaches her offspring over time, there is little hope for natural and adaptive adult behavior. Deforestation, poaching, bush meat trade, and exotic pet trade threaten chimps in the wild today where such maternal relationships are best fostered.

Do we share the ability for emotional attitudes and understanding with other primates or are we projecting our specific humanness on to their biological behavior? Anthropomorphism and anthropodenial are two terms we can use to probe for this difficult insight.

Is it nature or nurture that forms a primate's ability to share social bonds or to strike out aggressively? Are any primates naturally killer apes? Or nurtured to be violent? A new look at primate social behavior suggests we may be seeing the classic "nature vs. nurture" debate as an unproductive dichotomy.

Section III - Hominids TRANSFORMED AND TRANSFORMING

Early hominid adaptations in a social or physical environment are reconstructed from many small clues. New insight is often derived from the analysis of small elements such as body size (A), predation(B), analysis of important bones(C), or adaptation to a distinctive habitat (D).

Human adaptation to complex glacial environments can be traced deep into the past...but do our own human origins begin with a unique gene pool called Neandertal(A) or only appear in later ice ages with an explosion of new technology made by an anatomically modern humans(B). Wherever our humanness began, it led to a potential for overexploiting our environment(C).

Section IV - MAP QUIZES and EXERCISES

Chapter 1

Epistemology: How You Know What You Know

By Kenneth L. Feder

Knowing Things

The word *epistemology* means the study of knowledge—how you know what you know. Think about it. How does anybody know anything to be actual, truthful, or real? How do we differentiate fact from fantasy, the reasonable from the unreasonable, the meaningful from the meaningless—in archaeology or in any other field of knowledge? Everybody knows things, but how do we really know these things?

I know, for example, that there is a mountain in a place called Tibet. I know that the mountain is called by Westerners Everest and by Tibetans *Chomolungma* (Goddess of the Universe). I know that it is the tallest land mountain in the world (there are some a bit taller under the ocean). I'm even pretty sure how tall it is: 29,028 feet. But I have never measured it; I've never even been to Tibet. Beyond this, I have not measured all of the other mountains in the world to compare them to Everest. Yet I am quite confident that Everest is the world's tallest peak. But how do I know that?

On the subject of mountains, there is a run-down stone monument on the top of Bear Mountain in the northwestern corner of Connecticut. The monument was built toward the end of the nineteenth century and marks the "highest ground" in Connecticut (Figure 2.1). When the monument was built to memorialize this most lofty and auspicious of peaks—the mountain is all of 2,316 feet high—people knew that it was the highest point in the state and wanted to recognize this fact with the monument.

There is only one problem. In recent times, with more accurate, sophisticated measuring equipment, it has been determined that Bear Mountain is not the highest point in Connecticut. The slope of Frissell Mountain, which actually peaks in Massachusetts, reaches a height of 2,380 feet on the Connecticut side of the border, eclipsing Bear Mountain by about 64 feet.

So, people in the late 1800s and early 1900s "knew" that Bear Mountain was the highest point in Connecticut. Today we know that they really did not "know" that, because it was not true—even though they thought it was and built a monument saying so.

Now, suppose that I read in a newspaper, hear on the radio, or see on television a claim that another mountain has been

1

Figure 2.1 Plaque adorning a stone monument perched atop Bear Mountain in the northwestern corner of Connecticut. Note that the height of the mountain is given as 2,354 feet (it actually is only 2,316 feet) and, in either case, though memorialized as "the highest ground" in the state, it is not. (K. L. Feder)

found that is actually 10 (or 50, or 10,000) feet higher than Mount Everest. Indeed, just a few years ago, new satellite data convinced a few, just for a while, that a peak neighboring Everest was, in actuality, slightly higher. That measurement turned out to be in error. But what about the precise height of Everest itself?

Remember my statement that I am "pretty sure" that the height of Everest is 29,028 feet? You will find that number in virtually every book on world geography or geology, in every encyclopedia, and, in fact, in almost every published reference to the great peak—at least before November 1999. That number, 29,028 feet, was, until recently, part of our common knowledge about the world. And it turns out to be wrong, albeit by only a little bit. The quoted figure was determined in 1954 using the best technology available at the time. Our technology for doing such things as measuring elevations has improved radically in the intervening years. In a project sponsored by the National Geographic Society, a team of climbers ascended Everest in March 1999 to remeasure the "roof of the world." Using information gleaned from Global Positioning System satellites, it was determined that Everest is actually 7 feet higher, 29,035 feet high, and may be growing, if only by a small fraction of an inch each year, as a result of geological forces (Roach 1999).

One of the defining characteristics of science is its pursuit of modification and refinement of what we know and how we explain things. Scientists realize they have to be ever vigilant and, contrary to what some people seem to think, ever open to new information that enables us to tweak, polish, overhaul, or even overturn what we think we know. Science does not grudgingly admit the need for such refinement or reassessment but rather embraces it as a fundamental part of the scientific method.

But now back to Everest. You and I have likely never been to Tibet to personally assess or verify any measurement of the mountain. So what criteria can we use to determine if any of it is true or accurate? It all comes back to epistemology. How, indeed, do we know what we think we know?

Collecting Information: Seeing Isn't Necessarily Believing

In general, people collect information in two ways:

1. Directly through their own experiences

2. Indirectly through specific information sources such as friends, teachers, parents, books, TV, the Internet, and so forth

People tend to think that obtaining firsthand information—what they see or experience themselves—is always the best way. Unfortunately this is a false assumption because most people are poor observers.

For example, the list of animals that people claim to have observed—and that turn out to be figments of their imagination—is staggering. It is fascinating to read Pliny, a first-century thinker, or Topsell, who wrote in the seventeenth century, and see detailed accounts of the nature and habits of dragons, griffins, unicorns, mermaids, and so on (Byrne 1979). People claimed to have seen these animals, gave detailed descriptions, and even drew pictures of them (Figure 2.2). Many folks read their books and believed them.

Nor are untrained observers very good at identifying known, living animals. A red or "lesser" panda escaped from the zoo in Rotterdam, Holland, in December 1978. Red pandas are very rare animals indigenous to China, Tibet, Nepal, and Burma, not Holland. They are distinctive in appearance and cannot be readily mistaken for any other sort of animal. The zoo informed the press that the panda was missing, hoping the publicity would alert people in the area of the zoo and aid in the panda's return. Just when the newspapers came out with the panda story, it was found, quite dead, along some railroad tracks adjacent to the zoo. Nevertheless, over one hundred sightings of the panda *alive* were reported to the zoo from all over the Netherlands *after* the animal was obviously already dead. These reports did not stop until several days after the newspapers announced the discovery of the dead panda (van Kampen 1979). So much for the absolute reliability of firsthand observation.

Collecting Information: Relying on Others

In exploring the problems of secondhand information, we run into even more complications. When we are not in place to observe something firsthand, we are forced to rely on the quality of someone else's observations, interpretations, and reports—as with the reported height of Mount Everest.

In assessing a report made by others, you need to ask yourself several questions: How did they obtain the information in the first place—revelation, intuition, science? What are their motives for providing this information? What agenda—religious, philosophical, nationalistic, or otherwise—do they have? What is their source of information, and how expert are they in the topic?

Most people obtain information about the world and current events from established sources such as television news, books, or newspapers. Let's look at the last of these.

Figure 2.2 A seventeenth-century rendition of a clearly mythological beast—a *Mantichora*. The creature was considered to be real and was described as being the size of a wild ass, as having quills on its tail that it could hurl at adversaries, and as having a fondness for human flesh.

Not all newspapers are equally accurate and believable. The *New York Times* has a reputation for factual reporting and carries the following promise in its masthead: "All the News That's Fit to Print." No one, not even their publishers, would characterize tabloid papers like the *Enquirer*, the *Star*, the *Examiner*, the *Weekly World News*, or the *Sun* in those same terms (Bird 1992). When asked about the accuracy of some of the more bizarre stories that appear in his paper, the editor of the *Weekly World News* has been quoted as responding, "For heaven's sake, we entertain people. We make people feel better" (Johnson 1994:27). Notice there is nothing in that response that defends or maintains the accuracy of the stories.

The *Sun* is even more revealing in the disclaimer published in every edition: "*Sun* stories seek to entertain and are about the fantastic, bizarre, and paranormal. The reader should suspend belief for the sake of enjoyment." I presume this means "The reader should suspend *dis*belief for the sake of

enjoyment." In other words, leave your skepticism behind because this isn't serious stuff; even we don't believe most of it. Just read these weird and improbable stories for the entertainment value in them.

In fact, most people follow that advice. In her wonderful anthropological study of the tabloids, S. Elizabeth Bird (1992) shows that most people who read the tabloids regularly do so for the celebrity gossip (which occasionally turns out to be true) and for the uplifting human interest stories that are ignored by the popular press, as well as for the more bizarre material that adorns the pages of these publications. In terms of the latter, regular readers believe some (usually the stuff that reinforces previously held beliefs), but discard most of the rest, viewing it with a combination of interest and humor.

Anthropological topics do attract quite a bit of attention from the tabloids (see Figure 1.1). Mark Allen Peterson (1991), a writer with backgrounds in anthropology and journalism, classifies tabloid stories about anthropology into four categories:

1. *Aliens and ape men*—These stories usually assert some alleged connection between an isolated group of people and extraterrestrial aliens or Bigfoot.
2. *Whacky savages*—These stories focus on the "bizarre" (that term shows up a lot) antics of a tribal or "primitive" people. Sexual and marriage practices are closely scrutinized in these articles.
3. *Whacky anthropologists*—These are usually upbeat stories about anthropologists who are viewed as peculiar and eccentric intellectuals who travel to awful places to study odd, but nevertheless interesting, things.
4. *Silly studies*—These stories are somewhat similar in terms of topic to those included in category 3, but the perspective is quite different, being highly critical of the tax money "wasted" in supporting the frivolous studies conducted by those "whacky anthropologists."

Tabloid stories often are absurd, and few of the writers or even the readers believe them. This still leaves us with the broader question: How do we know what to believe? This is a crucial question that all rational people must ask themselves, whether talking about medicine, religion, archaeology, or anything else. Again, it comes back around to epistemology; how do we know what we think we know, and how do we know what or whom to believe?

Science: Playing by the Rules

There are ways to knowledge that are both dependable and reliable. We might not be able to get to absolute truths about the meaning of existence, but we can figure out quite a bit about our world—about chemistry and biology, psychology and sociology, physics and history, and even prehistory. The techniques used to get at knowledge we can feel confident in—knowledge that is reliable, truthful, and factual—are referred to as *science*.

In large part, science is a series of techniques used to maximize the probability that what we think we know really reflects the way things are, were, or will be. Science makes no claim to have all the answers or even to be right all the time. On the contrary, during the process of the growth of knowledge and understanding, science is often wrong. Remember that even as seemingly fundamental a fact as the height of the tallest mountain on earth is subject to reassessment and correction. The only claim that we do make in science is that if we honestly, consistently, and vigorously pursue knowledge using some basic techniques and principles, the truth will eventually surface and we can truly know things about the nature of the world in which we find ourselves.

The question then is, What exactly is science? Hollywood has a number of different stereotypes of scientists. Though there is the occasional female— typically bookish, shy, with thick eyeglasses and hair in a permanent bun—most movie scientist archetypes are white men: the wild-eyed and even

Figure 2.3 Gene Wilder depicted a stereotypical—and quite hilarious—mad scientist in the movie *Young Frankenstein*. As funny as his character was, it reflects a common, though quite mistaken, view of what real scientists are like and how they go about their research. (© Motion Picture & TV Photo Archive)

wilder-haired eccentric who mixes assorted chemicals in a dark, mysterious laboratory; the brilliant but egotistical young man who misuses the power of his remarkable discovery; the unkempt, nerdy, antisocial genius who is oblivious to the impact his work has on the world. The classic Doctor Frankenstein (Figure 2.3) comes immediately to mind.

So much for Hollywood. Scientists are not misfits or megalomaniacs without practical concerns or interests beyond their specialties. We are just people trying to arrive at some truths about how the world and the universe work. Although the application of science can be a slow, frustrating, all-consuming enterprise, the basic assumptions we scientists hold are very simple. Whether we are physicists, biologists, or archaeologists, we all work from four underlying principles. These principles are quite straightforward, but equally quite crucial.

1. There is a real and knowable universe.
2. The universe (which includes stars, planets, animals, and rocks, as well as people, their cultures, and their histories) operates according to certain understandable rules or laws.
3. These laws are immutable—that means they do not, in general, change depending on where you are or "when" you are.
4. These laws can be discerned, studied, and understood by people through careful observation, experimentation, and research.

Let's look at these assumptions one at a time.

There Is a Real and Knowable Universe

In science we have to agree that there is a real universe out there for us to study—a universe full of stars, animals, human history, and prehistory that exists whether we are happy with that reality or not.

Recently, it has become fashionable to deny this fundamental underpinning of science. A group of thinkers called *deconstructionists*, for example, believe that all science and history are merely artificial constructs, devoid of any objective reality or truth. For some deconstructionists, "history exists only in the minds of historians" (Shermer and Grobman 2000:26); the actual past, if there is one, can never be known. As scientists Kurt Gottfried and Kenneth Wilson (1997:545) state, the deconstructionists claim that "scientific knowledge is only a communal belief system with a dubious grip on reality." Deconstructionists try to take apart common beliefs in an attempt to show that much of what we think we know is purely subjective and culturally based.

To some deconstructionists, there is no absolute reality for science to observe or explain; there are only cultural constructs of the universe that are different among people in different societies and even different between men and women within the same culture. There is not one reality but many, and all are equally valid.

Deconstructionists describe science as a purely Western mode of thought, a mechanistic, antinature pattern based on inequality, capitalist exploitation, and patriarchy. The objective observation and understanding at the heart of the scientific approach are impossibilities; the things we see and the explanations we come up with are informed by who we are. (See Paul R. Gross and Norman Levitt's [1994] disturbing book *Higher*

Superstition: The Academic Left and Its Quarrel with Science for a detailed criticism of the deconstructionists.) Science, to the deconstructionists, is merely the Western "myth"; it is no more objective and no more "real" than nonscientific myths.

As Theodore Schick and Lewis Vaughn (1999) point out, however, if there is no such thing as objective truth, then no statements, including this one—or any of those made by the deconstructionists themselves—are objectively true. We could know nothing because there would be nothing to know. This is not a useful approach for human beings. Science simply is not the same as myth or oral tradition. Science demands rigorous testing and retesting, and it commonly rejects and discards previous conclusions about the world as a result of such testing. The same cannot be said for nonscientific explanations about how things work.

I suppose one could attempt to demonstrate the culturally subjective nature of the physical principle that two things cannot occupy the same place at the same time by, say, standing in front of a moving train. You probably will not see any deconstructionist attempting this anytime soon.

The Universe Operates According to Understandable Laws

In essence, what this means is that there are rules by which the universe works: Stars produce heat and light according to the laws of nuclear physics; nothing can go faster than the speed of light; all matter in the universe is attracted to all other matter (the law of gravity).

Though human societies are extremely complex systems and people may not operate according to rigid or unchanging rules of behavior, social scientists can nevertheless construct lawlike generalizations that accurately predict how human groups react to changes in their environment and how their cultures evolve through time. For example, development of complex civilizations in Egypt, China, India/Pakistan, Mesopotamia, Mexico, and Peru was not based on random processes (Haas 1982; Lamberg-Karlovsky and Sabloff 1995). Their evolution seems to reflect similar general patterns. This is not to say that all of these civilizations were identical, any more than we would say that all stars are identical. On the contrary, they existed in different physical and cultural environments, and so we should expect that they would be different. However, in each case the rise to civilization was preceded by development of an agricultural economy and socially stratified societies. In each case, civilization was also preceded by some degree of overall population increase as well as increased population density in some areas (in other words, the development of cities). Again, in each case we find monumental works (pyramids, temples), evidence of long-distance trade, and development of mathematics, astronomy, and methods of record keeping (usually, but not always, in the form of writing). The cultures in which civilization developed, though some were unrelated and independent, shared these factors because of the nonrandom patterns of cultural evolution.

The point is that everything operates according to rules. In science we believe that by understanding these rules or laws we can understand stars, organisms, and even ourselves.

The Laws Are Immutable

That the laws do not change under ordinary conditions is a crucial concept in science. A law that works here works there. A law that worked in the past will work today and will work in the future.

For example, if I go to the top of the Leaning Tower of Pisa today and simultaneously drop two balls of unequal mass, they will fall at the same rate and reach the ground at the same time, just as they did when Galileo performed a similar experiment in the seventeenth century. If I perform the same experiment countless times, the same thing will occur because the laws of the universe (in this case, the law of gravity) do not change through time. They also do not change depending on where you are. Go anywhere on the earth and perform the same experiment—you will get the same results (try not to hit any pedestrians or you will see some other "laws" in operation). This experiment was even performed by U.S. astronauts on the moon during the Apollo 15 mission. A hammer and a feather were dropped from the same height, and they hit the surface at precisely the same instant (the only reason this will not work on earth is because the feather is caught by the air and the hammer, obviously, is not). We have no reason to believe that the results would be different anywhere or "anywhen" else.

If this assumption of science, that the laws do not change through time, were false, many of the so-called historical sciences, including prehistoric archaeology, could not exist.

For example, historical geologists are interested in knowing how the various landforms we see today came into being. They recognize that they cannot go back in time to see how the Grand Canyon was formed. However, because the laws of geology that governed the development of the Grand Canyon have not changed through time and because these laws are still in operation, historical geologists can study the formation of geological features today and apply what they learn to the past. The same laws they can directly study operating in the present were operating in the past when geological features that interest them first formed.

In the words of nineteenth-century geologist Charles Lyell, the "present" we can observe is the "key" to understanding the past that we cannot. This is true because the laws, or rules, that govern the universe are constant—those that operate today operated in the past. This is why science does not limit itself to the present but makes inferences about the past and even predictions about the future (listen to the weather report for an example of this). We can do so because we can study modern, ongoing phenomena that work under the same laws that existed in the past and will exist in the future.

This is where science and theology are often forced to part company and respectfully disagree. Remember, science depends on the constancy of the laws that we can discern. In contrast, advocates of many religions, though they might believe that there are laws that

govern things (and which, according to them, were established by a Creator), usually (but not always) believe that these laws can be changed at any time by their God. In other words, if God does not want the apple to fall to the ground but instead wants it to hover, violating the law of gravity, that is precisely what will happen. As a more concrete example, scientists know that the heat and light given off by a fire result from the transformation of mass (of the wood) to energy. Physical laws control this process. A theologian, however, might agree with this ordinarily but feel that if God wants to create a fire that does not consume any mass (like the "burning bush" seen by Moses in the Old Testament), then this is exactly what will occur. Most scientists simply do not accept this assertion. The rules are the rules. They do not change, even though we might sometimes wish that they would.

The Laws Can Be Understood

This may be the single most important principle in science. The universe is, theoretically at least, knowable. It may be complicated, and it may take years and years to understand even apparently simple phenomena. Each attempt at understanding leads us to collect more data and to test, reevaluate, and refine our proposed explanations—for how planets formed, why a group of animals became extinct while another thrived, or how a group of ancient people responded to a change in their natural environment, contact with an alien group of people, or adoption of a new technology. We rarely get it right the first time and are continually collecting new information, abandoning some interpretations while refining others. We constantly rethink our explanations. In this way, little by little, bit by bit, we expand our knowledge and understanding. Through this kind of careful observation and objective research and experimentation, we can indeed know things.

So, our assumptions are simple enough. We accept the existence of a reality independent of our own minds, and we accept that this reality works according to a series of unchanging laws or rules. We also claim that we can recognize and understand these laws, or at least recognize the patterns that result from these universal rules. The question remains then: How do we do science— how do we explore the nature of the universe, whether our interest is planets, stars, atoms, or human prehistory?

The Workings of Science

We can know things by employing the rules of logic and rational thought. Scientists—archaeologists or otherwise—usually work through a combination of the logical processes known as *induction* and *deduction*. The dictionary definition of induction is "arguing from specifics to generalities," whereas deduction is defined as the reverse, arguing from generalities to specifics.

What is essential to good science is objective, unbiased observations—of planets, molecules, rock formations, archaeological sites, and so on. Often, on the basis of these specific observations, we induce explanations called *hypotheses* for how these things work.

For example, we may study the planets Mercury, Venus, Earth, and Mars (each one presents specific bits of

information). We then induce general rules about how we think these inner planets in our solar system were formed. Or we might study a whole series of different kinds of molecules and then induce general rules about how all molecules interact chemically. We may study different rock formations and make general conclusions about their origin. We can study a number of specific prehistoric sites and make generalizations about how cultures evolved.

Notice that we cannot directly observe planets forming, the rules of molecular interaction, rocks being made, or prehistoric cultures evolving. Instead, we are inducing general conclusions and principles concerning our data that seem to follow logically from what we have been able to observe.

This process of induction, though crucial to science, is not enough. We need to go beyond our induced hypotheses by testing them. If our induced hypotheses are indeed valid—that is, if they really represent the actual rules according to which some aspect of the universe (planets, molecules, rocks, ancient societies) works—they should be able to hold up under the rigors of scientific hypothesis testing.

Observation and the suggestion of hypotheses, therefore, are only the first steps in a scientific investigation. In science we always need to go beyond observation and hypothesizing. We need to set up a series of "if . . . then" statements; "if" our hypothesis is true, "then" the following deduced "facts" will also be true. Our results are not always precise and clear-cut, especially in a science like archaeology, but this much should be clear—scientists are not just out there collecting a bunch of interesting facts. Facts are always collected within the context of trying to explain something or of trying to test a hypothesis.

As an example of this logical process, consider the health effects of smoking. How can scientists be sure that smoking is bad for you? After all, it's pretty rare that someone takes a puff on a cigarette and immediately drops dead. The certainty comes from a combination of induction and deduction. Observers have noticed for about 300 years that people who smoked seemed to be more likely to get certain diseases than people who did not smoke. As long ago as the seventeenth century, people noticed that habitual pipe smokers were subject to tumor growths on their lips and in their mouths. From such observations we can reasonably, though tentatively, induce a hypothesis of the unhealthfulness of smoking, but we still need to test such a hypothesis. We need to set up "if . . . then" statements. If, in fact, smoking is a hazard to your health (the hypothesis we have induced based on our observations), then we should be able to deduce some predictions that must also be true. Sure enough, when we test specific, deduced predictions such as

1. Smokers will have a higher incidence of lung cancer than nonsmokers
2. Smokers will have a higher incidence of emphysema
3. Smokers will take more sick days from work
4. Smokers will get more upper-respiratory infections
5. Smokers will have diminished lung capacity

6. Smokers will have a shorter life expectancy

we see that our original, induced hypothesis—cigarette smoking is hazardous to your health—is upheld.

That was easy, but also obvious. How about an example with more mystery to it, one in which scientists—acting like detectives—had to solve a puzzle to save lives?

The Case of Childbed Fever

In nineteenth-century Europe, the hospital could be a very dangerous place for a woman about to give birth. Death rates in some so-called lying-in wards were horrifically high, the result of what became known as "childbed fever." A seemingly healthy young woman would arrive at the hospital with an unremarkable pregnancy, experience a normal labor, and give birth to a healthy baby. Over the course of the hours and days following birth, however, she might exhibit a rapid pulse, high fever, distended and painful abdomen, foul discharge, and delirium—and then would die.

Oddly, while childbed fever took a horrible toll in hospital deliveries, it was rare or absent in home births. In fact, as Sherwin Nuland (2003:97), physician and author of a fascinating book on childbed fever points out, a woman was generally much safer if she gave birth on the street or in an alley on her way to the hospital than if she actually arrived there. For example, carefully maintained mortality statistics show that between 1831 and 1843 in London, approximately 10 out of 10,000 home births resulted in the death of the mother, while in the hospital the death rate was 60 times higher; 600 out of 10,000 died (Nuland 2003:41). In France, similar statistics show that, between 1833 and 1842, the death rate for mothers giving birth in hospitals in Paris was as high as 880 per 10,000 (Nuland 2003:41). By way of comparison, in the United States today, on average, for every 10,000 births there is only about a single maternal death (Chang et al. 2003).

In the nineteenth century, there were two wards, or divisions, at the Vienna General Hospital in Austria. Each year between 6,000 and 7,000 women arrived at the gates of the hospital to give birth, and an equal number ended up in each of the two divisions. In Division 2, in a given year, on average, about 60 women died soon after giving birth, a death rate of about 2 percent. Astonishingly, in Division 1, in the same hospital, the number of yearly deaths was more than ten times higher, with more than 600 and as many as 800 dying in a given year, a terrifying death rate as high as 27 percent (Nuland 2003:97).

Physicians were, needless to say, appalled by such statistics. Performing autopsies on patients who had died in the hospital had become a regular practice in the nineteenth century in Europe. Many doctors carefully examined the bodies of the women who had died of childbed fever and found them ravaged by an aggressive infection and filled with an intensely foul smelling whitish fluid. Many of these physicians were more than willing to propose hypotheses suggesting possible causes of the condition. Perhaps, it was suggested, tight petticoats worn early in pregnancy were involved, leading to a woman's inability to expel fluids after giving

birth. Or perhaps it was the foul air in hospitals with their closed-in spaces. Magnetic fields and atmospheric disturbances were blamed. Perhaps some women simply were predisposed to having their milk ducts get blocked and then dying when milk deteriorated inside of them; the whiteness of the infection seen in autopsy was assumed by some to indicate its source as soured mother's milk. Others, aware that home births with their very low rates of childbed fever were attended to by midwives, all of whom were themselves women, suggested that the condition was the result of female modesty.

In other words, childbed fever afflicted women who were particularly embarrassed by being examined by male doctors and medical students. Some even proposed the wonderfully circular explanation that childbed fever had a psychological origin, the result of the great fear many women had of the hospital because of the possibility of contracting childbed fever!

Back in Vienna at the General Hospital, Ignaz Semmelweis, a young Hungarian doctor who had been turned down for a couple of plum assignments, ended up, by default, in obstetrics. Determined to solve the childbed fever riddle, Semmelweis realized that the General Hospital, with its two divisions having very different mortality rates, presented a unique opportunity to experimentally test the various hypotheses proposed to explain childbed fever.

Semmelweis immediately rejected those proposed explanations that didn't differentiate the two divisions. For example, one doctor suggested that childbed fever was caused by badly maintained hospital walls, but the walls were in equal disrepair in both divisions, and the mortality rates were entirely different, so it was pointless to pursue this explanation. While outright rejecting hypotheses related to atmospheric conditions, earth energies, and dirty walls, Semmelweis and some of his colleagues at the hospital recognized a handful of genuine and potentially important differences between the two obstetrical divisions in the hospital and induced a series of possible explanations for the drastic difference in their mortality rates. They suggested:

1. Division 1 tended to be more crowded than Division 2. The overcrowding in Division 1 was a possible cause of the higher mortality rate there.
2. Women in Division 2 were assisted by midwives who directed the women to deliver on their sides, while those in Division 1 were attended to by physicians and medical students who kept women on their backs during delivery. Birth position was a possible cause of the higher mortality rate.
3. There was a psychological factor involved; the hospital priest had to walk through Division 1 to administer the last rites to dying patients in other wards. Perhaps this sight so upset some women already weakened by the ordeal of childbirth that it contributed to their deaths.
4. Unlike the women in Division 2, who were assisted by experienced midwives using far less invasive techniques, the women in Division 1 were attended to by medical students being trained in obstetrics. Perhaps all of the additional poking and prodding conducted during this

training was harmful and contributed to the higher death rate of women in Division 1.

These induced hypotheses all sounded good. Each marked a genuine difference between Divisions 1 and 2 that might have caused the difference in the death rate. Semmelweis was doing what most scientists do in such a situation; he was relying on creativity and imagination in seeking out an explanation.

Creativity and imagination are just as important to science as good observation. But being creative and imaginative was not enough. It did not help the women who were still dying at an alarming rate. Semmelweis had to go beyond producing possible explanations; he had to test each one of them. So, he deduced the necessary implications of each:

1. If hypothesis 1 were correct, then alleviating the crowding in Division 1 should reduce the mortality rate. The result: no change. So the first hypothesis was rejected. It had failed the scientific test; it simply could not be correct.
2. Semmelweis went on to test hypothesis 2 by changing the birth positions of the women in Division 1 to match those of the women in Division 2. Again, there was no change, and another hypothesis was rejected.
3. Next, to test hypothesis 3, the priest was rerouted. Women in Division 1 continued to die of childbed fever at about five times the rate of those in Division 2.
4. To test hypothesis 4, it was decided to limit the number of invasive procedures used on the women to

train the students in their examination techniques. This was accomplished by limiting the number of students who actually examined the women. Specifically, the many non-Austrian students in the obstetrics program were restricted from examining these patients, while the native Austrians continued to be trained in the ward. The statistics showed that this had no impact on the death rate in Division 1; 10 or 11 percent of the women continued to die even when fewer students were allowed to examine them internally.

Then, as so often happens in science, Semmelweis had a stroke of luck. An acquaintance—also a doctor—died, and the manner of his death provided Semmelweis with another possible explanation for the problem in Division 1. Though Semmelweis's friend was not a woman who had recently given birth, he did have precisely the same symptoms as did the women who were dying of childbed fever. Most important, this doctor had died of a disease similar to childbed fever soon after accidentally cutting himself during an autopsy.

Viruses and bacteria were unknown in the 1840s. Surgical instruments were not sterilized, no special effort was made to clean the hands, and doctors did not wear gloves during operations and autopsies. Supposing that there was something bad in dead bodies and this something had entered Semmelweis's friend's system through his wound—could the same bad "stuff" (Semmelweis called it "cadaveric material") get onto the hands of the physicians and medical students, who then might, without washing, go on to help a woman give birth? Then, if this "cadaveric material"

were transmitted into the woman's body during the birth of her baby, it might lead to her death.

This possibility inspired Semmelweis's final hypothesis: The presence of physicians and medical students in Division 1 was at the root of the mystery. Students who attended the women in Division 1 regularly conducted autopsies as part of their training and so would be in contact with dead bodies on the same days they were assisting women giving birth. Furthermore, physicians would frequently perform autopsies on the bodies of women who had already died of childbed fever, often going directly from the autopsy room to the birthing rooms to assist other women giving birth. Herein was a grimly ironic twist to this new hypothesis; the attempt by physicians to solve the mystery of childbed fever by performing autopsies on its victims was one of the most important factors in transmitting the disease to additional women.

To test this hypothesis, Semmelweis instituted new policies in Division 1, including the requirement that all attending physicians and students cleanse their hands with chlorine before entering. The result: The death rate among women birthing in Division 1 dropped to between 1 and 2 percent, exactly the rate in Division 2. Semmelweis had both solved the mystery and halted an epidemic.

Science and Nonscience: The Essential Differences

Through objective observation and analysis, a scientist, whether a physicist, chemist, biologist, psychologist, or archaeologist, sees things that need explaining. Through creativity and imagination, the scientist suggests possible hypotheses to explain these "mysteries." The scientist then sets up a rigorous method through experimentation or subsequent research to deductively test the validity of a given hypothesis. If the implications of a hypothesis are shown not to be true, the hypothesis must be rejected and then it's back to the drawing board. If the implications are found to be true, we can uphold or support our hypothesis.

A number of other points should be made here. The first is that for a hypothesis, whether it turns out to be upheld or not, to be scientific, it must be testable. In other words, there must be clear, deduced implications that can be drawn from the hypothesis and then tested. Remember the hypotheses of "magnetic fields" and "atmospheric disturbances"? How can you test these? What are the necessary implications that can be deduced from the hypothesis "More women died in Division 1 because of atmospheric disturbances"? There really aren't any, and therefore such a hypothesis is not scientific—it cannot be tested. Remember, in the methodology of science, we ordinarily need to

1. Observe
2. Induce general hypotheses or possible explanations for what we have observed
3. Deduce specific things that must also be true if our hypothesis is true
4. Test the hypothesis by checking out the deduced implications

As Michael Shermer (1997:19) points out, "Science, of course, is not this rigid, and no scientist consciously goes through 'steps.' The process is a constant interaction of making observations, drawing conclusions, making predictions, and checking them against evidence."

Testing a hypothesis is crucial. If there are no specific implications of a hypothesis that can then be analyzed as a test of the validity or usefulness of that hypothesis, then you simply are not doing and cannot do "science."

For example, suppose you observe a person who appears to be able to "guess" the value of a playing card picked from a deck. Next, assume that someone hypothesizes that "psychic" ability is involved. Finally, suppose the claim is made that the "psychic" ability goes away as soon as you try to test it (actually named the "shyness effect" by some researchers of the paranormal). Such a claim is not itself testable and therefore not scientific.

Beyond the issue of testability, another lesson is involved in determining whether an approach to a problem is scientific. Semmelweis induced four different hypotheses to explain the difference in mortality rates between Divisions 1 and 2. These "competing" explanations are called *multiple working hypotheses*. Notice that Semmelweis did not simply proceed by a process of elimination. He did not, for example, test the first three hypotheses and—after finding them invalid—declare that the fourth was necessarily correct because it was the only one left that he had thought of.

Some people try to work that way. A light is seen in the sky. Someone hypothesizes it was a meteor. We find out that it was not. Someone else hypothesizes that it was a military rocket. Again this turns out to be incorrect. Someone else suggests that it was the Goodyear blimp, but that turns out to have been somewhere else. Finally, someone suggests that it was the spacecraft of people from another planet. Some will say that this must be correct because none of the other explanations panned out. This is nonsense. There are plenty of other possible explanations. Eliminating all of the explanations *we* have been able to think of except one (which, perhaps, has no testable implications) in no way allows us to uphold that final hypothesis. You will see just such an error in logic with regard to the Shroud of Turin artifact discussed in Chapter 11.

A Rule in Assessing Explanations

Finally, there is another rule to hypothesis making and testing. It is called *Occam's razor* or *Occam's rule*. In thinking, in trying to solve a problem, or in attempting to explain some phenomenon, "Entities are not to be multiplied beyond necessity." In other words, the explanation or hypothesis that explains a series of observations with the fewest other assumptions or leaps—the hypothesis that does not multiply these entities beyond necessity—is the best explanation.

Here's an example. My archaeology class was to begin in about ten minutes, and the previous class was just dispersing from what had obviously been a raucous session. As I entered the room, I noticed the three-dimensional, geometric shapes made of heavy stock paper suspended by string from the seminar room ceiling. I caught the attention of the professor, a truly gentle soul and one of the nicest people I had met in my first year of teaching, and I asked the obvious question: "What's the deal with the shapes?" She smiled and launched into a passionate discourse

Figure 2.4 An 1827 lithograph of a fossil quarry in the Tilgate Forest, Sussex, England. Workers are extracting a dinosaur bone from a large rock fragment. (From Mantell's Geology of Sussex)

about the exercise just conducted by the class—an experiment in "psychokinesis," the ostensible ability to move or otherwise affect objects simply by the power of thought. Perhaps my jaw dropped a little too obviously, and my colleague asked, "Would you like to see me do it?" Without waiting for a response, she gazed up at the shape directly above her head and closed her eyes; when she opened them we both looked up to see the suspended object swaying back and forth. "See?" she said.

Before you get too terribly excited about this demonstration, perhaps I should add that it was a rather breezy day and the windows in the seminar room were wide open. The object toward which my colleague had directed her ostensibly paranormal talents indeed was moving, but so were all of the other suspended objects, as were papers on the desk at the front of the class and just about anything else that wasn't nailed down. I pointed out that, just perhaps, the suspended object was moving simply because of the wind. My colleague just smiled broadly, patted me on the shoulder, and said, "Oh Kenny, you're such a skeptic." Indeed I am, and in this story rests the essence of Occam's razor. Could the object have been moving as the result of my colleague's psychokinetic prowess? Well, yes. But it also could have been moving as a result of open windows and wind. Which explanation— psychokinesis or wind—requires the least violence to our understanding of reality? Which requires the fewest logical leaps or as yet unsupported assumptions about how the universe operates? Occam's razor directs the gambler in reality's casino to bet on the sure thing or, at least, the surer thing, until a preponderance of evidence convinces one otherwise. In this particular case, I'm betting on the wind.

Here's another example. During the eighteenth and nineteenth centuries, huge buried, fossilized bones were found throughout North America and Europe (Figure 2.4). One hypothesis, the simplest, was that the bones were the remains of animals that no longer existed. This hypothesis simply relied on the assumption that bones do not come into existence by themselves but always serve as the skeletons of animals. Therefore, when you find bones, there must have been animals who used those bones. However, another hypothesis was suggested: The bones were deposited by the Devil to fool us into thinking that such animals existed (Howard 1975). This hypothesis "multiplied" those "entities" Occam warned us about. This explanation demanded many more assumptions about the universe than did the first: There is a Devil, that Devil is interested in human affairs, he wants to fool us, he has the ability to make bones of animals that never existed, and he has the ability to hide them under the ground and inside solid rock. That is quite a number of unproven (and largely untestable) claims to swallow.

Thus, Occam's razor says the simpler hypothesis, that these great bones are evidence of the existence of animals that no longer exist—in other words, dinosaurs—is better. The other explanation raises more questions than it answers.

The Art of Science

Don't get the impression that science is a mechanical enterprise. Science is at least partially an art. It is much more than just observing the results of experiments.

It takes great creativity to recognize a "mystery" in the first place. In the apocryphal story, countless apples had fallen from countless trees and undoubtedly conked the noggins of multitudes of stunned individuals who never thought much about it. It took a fabulously creative individual, Isaac Newton, to even recognize that herein lay a mystery. Why did the apple fall? It could have hovered in midair. It could have moved off in any of the cardinal directions. It could have gone straight up and out of sight. But it did not. It fell to the ground as it always had, in all places, and as it always would. It took great imagination to recognize that in this simple observation (and in a bump on the head) rested the eloquence of a fundamental law of the universe.

Where Do Hypotheses Come From?

Coming up with hypotheses is not a simple or mechanical procedure. The scientific process requires creativity. Hypotheses arrive as often in flashes of insight as through plodding, methodical observation. Consider this example.

My field crew and I had just finished excavating the 2,000-year-old Loomis II archaeological site in Connecticut where a broad array of different kinds of stones had been used for making tools. Some of the "lithics" came from sources close to the site. Other sources were located at quite a distance, as much as a few hundred miles away. These nonnative "exotic" lithics were universally superior; tools could be made more easily from the nonlocal materials, and the edges produced were much sharper.

At the time the site was being excavated, I noticed that there seemed to be a pattern in terms of the size of the individual tools we were recovering. Tools made from the locally available and generally inferior materials of quartz and basalt were relatively large, and the pieces of rock that showed no evidence of use—archaeologists call these discarded pieces *debitage*—were also relatively large. In contrast, the tools made from the superior materials—a black flint and two kinds of jasper—that originated at a great distance from the site were much smaller. Even inconsequential flakes of exotic stone—pieces you could barely hold between two fingers—showed evidence of use, and only the tiniest of flakes was discarded without either further modification for use or evidence of use, such as for scraping, cutting, or piercing.

I thought it was an interesting pattern but didn't think much of it until about a year later when I was cleaning up the floor of my lab after a class in experimental archaeology where students were replicating stone tools. We used a number of different raw materials in the class, and just as was the case for the site, stone of inferior quality was readily available a few miles away, whereas more desirable material was from more distant sources.

As I cleaned up, I noticed that the discarded stone chips left by the students included perfectly serviceable pieces of the locally available, easy-toobtain stone, and only the tiniest fragments of flint and obsidian. We obtained flint in New York State from a source about 80 miles from campus, and we received obsidian from Wyoming. Suddenly it was clear to me that the pattern apparent at the archaeological site was repeating itself nearly two thousand years later among my students. More "valuable" stone—functionally superior and difficult to obtain—was used more efficiently, and there was far less waste than in stone that was easy to obtain and more difficult to work. I could now phrase this insight as a hypothesis and test it using the site data: More valuable lithic materials were used more efficiently at the Loomis II archaeological site (Feder 1981). In fact, by a number of measurements, this turned out to be precisely the case. The hypothesis itself came to me when I wasn't thinking of anything in particular; I was simply sweeping the floor.

It may take great skill and imagination to invent a hypothesis in the attempt to understand why things seem to work the way they do. Remember, Division 1 at the Vienna General Hospital did not have written over its doors, "Overcrowded Division" or "Division with Student Doctors Who Don't Wash Their Hands After Autopsies." It took imagination, first, to recognize that there were differences between the divisions and, second, to hypothesize that some of the differences might logically be at the root of the mystery. After all, there were in all likelihood many differences between the divisions: their compass orientations, the names of the nurses, the precise alignment of the windows, the astrological signs of the doctors who worked in the divisions, and so on. If a scientist were to attempt to test all of these differences as hypothetical causes of a mystery, nothing would ever be solved. Occam's razor must be applied. We need to focus our intellectual energies on those possible explanations

that require few other assumptions. Only after all of these have been eliminated can we legitimately consider others. As summarized by that great fictional detective, Sherlock Holmes:

> It is of the highest importance in the art of detection to be able to recognize, out of a number of facts, which are incidental and which are vital. Otherwise, your energy and attention must be dissipated instead of being concentrated. (Doyle 1891–1902:275)

Semmelweis concentrated his attention on first four, then a fifth possible explanation. Like all good scientists he had to use some amount of what we can call "intuition" to sort out the potentially vital from the probably incidental. Even in the initial sorting we may be wrong. Overcrowding, birth position, and psychological trauma seemed like very plausible explanations to Semmelweis, but they were wrong nonetheless.

Testing Hypotheses

Finally, it takes skill and inventiveness to suggest ways for testing the hypothesis in question. We must, out of our own heads, be able to invent the "then" part of our "if . . . then" statements. We need to be able to suggest those things that must be true if our hypothesis is to be supported. There really is an art to that. Anyone can claim there was a Lost Continent of Atlantis (Chapter 7), but often it takes a truly inventive mind to suggest precisely what archaeologists must find if the hypothesis of its existence is indeed to be validated.

Semmelweis tested his hypotheses and solved the mystery of childbed fever by changing conditions in Division 1 to see if the death rate would change. In essence, testing each hypothesis was an experiment.

It might seem obvious that medical researchers, physicists, or chemists working in labs can perform experiments, observe the results, and come to reasonable conclusions about what transpired. But how about the historical disciplines, including historical geology, history, and prehistoric archaeology? Researchers in these fields cannot go back in time to be there when the events they are attempting to describe and explain took place. Can they really know what happened in the past?

Yes, they can, by what historians Michael Shermer and Alex Grobman (2000:32) call a "convergence of evidence." For example, in their book *Denying History: Who Says the Holocaust Never Happened and Why Do They Say It?* they respond to those who deny that the Germans attempted to exterminate the Jewish population of Europe in the 1930s and 1940s. After all, even though that era isn't ancient history, we still can't return to observe it for ourselves, so how do we know what really happened? Shermer and Grobman marshal multiple sources of evidence, including documents like letters, speeches, blueprints, and articles where Germans discussed their plans; eyewitness accounts of individual atrocities; photographs showing the horror of the camps; the physical remains of the camps themselves; inferential evidence like demographic data showing that approximately 6 million European Jews disappeared during this period. Though we cannot travel back in time to the 1940s, these

different and independent lines of evidence converge, allowing us to conclude with absolute certainty that a particular historical event—in this case, the Holocaust—actually happened. Indeed, we can know what happened in history—and prehistory.

Ultimately, whether a science is experimentally based or not makes little logical difference in testing hypotheses. Instead of predicting what the results of a given experiment must be if our induced hypothesis is useful or valid, we predict what new data we must be able to find if a given hypothesis is correct.

For instance, we may hypothesize that long-distance trade is a key element in the development of civilization based on our analysis of the ancient Maya. We deduce that if this is correct—if this is, in fact, a general rule of cultural evolution—then we must find large quantities of trade items in other parts of the world where civilization also developed. We might further deduce that these items should be found in contexts that denote their value and importance to the society (for example, in the burials of leaders). We must then determine the validity of our predictions and, indirectly, our hypothesis by going out and conducting more research. We need to excavate sites belonging to other ancient civilizations and see if they followed the same pattern as seen for the Maya relative to the importance of trade.

Testing of hypotheses takes a great deal of thought, and we can make mistakes. We must remember: We have a hypothesis, we have the deduced implications, and we have the test. We can make errors at any place within this process—the hypothesis may be incorrect, the implications may be wrong, or the way we test them may be incorrect. Scientists are not perfect, and biases and preconceptions can interfere with this process. Certainty in science is a scarce commodity. There are always new hypotheses, alternative explanations, and more deductive implications to test. Nothing is ever finished, nothing is set in concrete, nothing is ever defined or raised to the level of religious truth.

The Human Enterprise of Science

Science is a very human endeavor practiced by imperfect human beings. Scientists are not isolated from the cultures and times in which they live. They share many of the same prejudices and biases of other members of their societies. Scientists learn from mentors at universities and inherit their perspectives. It often is quite difficult to go against the scientific grain, to question accumulated wisdom, and to suggest a new approach or perspective.

Consider the case of meteors. Today we take it for granted that sometimes quite large, extraterrestrial, natural objects go streaking across the sky and sometimes even strike the ground (then they are called meteorites). You may even be aware that major meteor showers can be seen twice a year: the Perseid shower in August and the Leonid shower in November. Perhaps you have been lucky enough to see a major meteor or "bolide," an awesome example of nature's fireworks. But until about two hundred years ago the notion that solid stone or metallic objects originating in space regularly enter the earth's atmosphere and sometimes strike the

ground was controversial and, in fact, rejected by most scientists. In 1704 Sir Isaac Newton categorically rejected the notion that there could be meteors because he did not believe there could be any cosmological source for them.

The quality of an argument and the evidence marshalled in its support should be all that matters in science. The authority or reputation of the scientist should not matter. Nevertheless, not many scientists were willing to go against the considered opinion of as bright a scientific luminary as Isaac Newton. Even so, a few brave thinkers risked their reputations by concluding that meteors really did originate in outer space. Their work was roundly criticized, at least for a time. But science is "self-corrective." Hypotheses are constantly being refined and retested as new data are collected.

In 1794, over the skies of Siena, Italy, there was a spectacular shower of about three thousand meteors, seen by tens of thousands of people (Cowen 1995). Even then, a nonmeteoric explanation was suggested. By coincidence, Mount Vesuvius had erupted just eighteen hours before the shower, and some tried to blame the volcano for being the source of the objects flaming in the skies over Italy.

Critics did what they could to dispel the "myth" of an extraterrestrial source for the streaks of light over Siena, but they could not succeed. Further investigation of subsequent major meteor falls in the late 1700s and early 1800s, as well as examination of the chemical makeup of some of the objects that had actually fallen from the sky (an iron and nickel alloy not found on earth), convinced

Table 2.1 *Books That Explain the Scientific Method*

Author	Book Title	Year	Publisher
Stephen Carey	*A Beginner's Guide to Scientific Method*	1998	Wadsworth
Thomas Gilovich	*How We Know What Isn't So*	1991	Free Press
Howard Kahane	*Logic and Contemporary Rhetoric: The Use of Reason in Everyday Life*	1998	Wadsworth
Robert Park	*Voodoo Science: The Road from Foolishness to Fraud*	2000	Oxford University Press
Daisie Radner and Michael Radner	*Science and Unreason*	1982	Wadsworth
Milton Rothman	*The Science Gap: Dispelling Myths and Understanding the Reality of Science*	1992	Prometheus Books
Carl Sagan	*The Demon-Haunted World*	1996	Random House
Michael Shermer	*Why People Believe Weird Things*	1997	W. H. Freeman
Theodore Schick and Lewis Vaughn	*Thinking About Weird Things: Critical Thinking for a New Age*	1999	Mayfield
Lewis Wolpert	*The Unnatural Nature of Science*	1993	Harvard University Press
Charles Wynn and Arthur Wiggins	*Quantum Leaps in the Wrong Direction*	2001	Joseph Henry Press

most by the early nineteenth century that meteors are what we now know them to be—extraterrestrial chunks of stone or metal that flame brightly when they enter our planet's atmosphere.

Philosopher of science Thomas Kuhn (1970) has suggested that the growth of scientific knowledge is not neatly linear, with knowledge simply building on knowledge. He maintains that science remains relatively static for periods and that most thinkers work under the same set of assumptions—the same *paradigm*. New ideas or perspectives, like those of Semmelweis or Einstein, that challenge the existing orthodoxy are usually initially rejected. Only once scientists get over the shock of the new ideas and start testing the new frameworks suggested by these new paradigms are great jumps in knowledge made.

That is why in science we propose, test, tentatively accept, but never prove a hypothesis. We keep only those hypotheses that cannot be disproved. As long as a hypothesis holds up under the scrutiny of additional testing through experiment and is not contradicted by new data, we accept it as the best explanation so far. Some hypotheses sound good, pass the rigors of initial testing, but are later shown to be inadequate or invalid. Others—for example, the hypothesis of biological evolution—have held up so well (all new data either were or could have been deduced from it) that they will probably always be upheld. We usually call these very well supported hypotheses *theories.* However, it is in the nature of science that no matter how well an explanation of some aspect of reality has held up, we must always be prepared to consider new tests and better explanations.

We are interested in knowledge and explanations of the universe that work. As long as these explanations work, we keep them. As soon as they cease being effective because new data and tests show them to be incomplete or misguided, we discard them and seek new ones. In one sense, Semmelweis was wrong after all, though his explanation worked at the time—he did save lives through its application. We now know that there is nothing inherently bad in "cadaveric material." Dead bodies are not the cause of childbed fever. Today we realize that it is bacteria that can grow in the flesh of a dead body that can get on a doctor's hands, infect a pregnant woman, and cause her death. Semmelweis worked in a time before the existence of such things was known. Science in this way always grows, expands, and evolves. See Table 2.1 for a number of works that discuss the method of science.

Science and Archaeology

The study of the human past is a science and relies on the same general logical processes that all sciences do. Unfortunately, perhaps as a result of its popularity, the data of archaeology have often been used by people to attempt to prove some idea or claim. Too often, these attempts have been bereft of science.

Chapter 2

Dr. Darwin

With a nod to evolution's god, physicians are looking at illness through the lens of natural selection to find out why we get sick and what we can do about it.

Lori Oliwenstein

PAUL EWALD KNEW FROM THE BEGINNING that the Ebola virus outbreak in Zaire would fizzle out. On May 26, after eight days in which only six new cases were reported, that fizzle became official. The World Health Organization announced it would no longer need to update the Ebola figures daily (though sporadic cases continued to be reported until June 20).

The virus had held Zaire's Bandundu Province in its deadly grip for weeks, infecting some 300 people and killing 80 percent of them. Most of those infected hailed from the town of Kikwit. It was all just as Ewald predicted. "When the Ebola outbreak occurred," he recalls, "I said, as I have before, these things are going to pop up, they're going to smolder, you'll have a bad outbreak of maybe 100 or 200 people in a hospital, maybe you'll have the outbreak slip into another isolated community, but then it will peter out on its own."

"If you look at it from an evolutionary point of view, you can sort out the 95 percent of disease organisms that aren't a major threat from the 5 percent that are."

Ewald is no soothsayer. He's an evolutionary biologist at Amherst College in Massachusetts and perhaps the world's leading expert on how infectious diseases—and the organisms that cause them—evolve. He's also a force behind what some are touting as the next great medical revolution: the application of Darwin's theory of natural selection to the understanding of human diseases.

A Darwinian view can shed some light on how Ebola moves from human to human once it has entered the population. (Between human outbreaks, the virus resides in some as yet unknown living reservoir.) A pathogen can survive in a population, explains Ewald, only if it can easily transmit its progeny from one host to another. One way to do this is to take a long time to disable a host, giving him plenty of time to come into contact with other potential victims. Ebola, however, kills quickly, usually in less than a week. Another way is to survive for a long time outside the human body, so that the pathogen can wait for new hosts to find it. But the Ebola strains encountered thus far are destroyed almost at once by sunlight, and even if no rays reach them, they tend to lose their infectiousness outside the human body within a day. "If you look at it from an evolutionary point of view, you can sort out the 95 percent of disease organisms that aren't a major threat from the 5 percent that are," says Ewald. "Ebola really isn't one of those 5 percent."

The earliest suggestion of a Darwinian approach to medicine came in 1980, when George Williams, an evolutionary biologist at the State University of New York at Stony Brook, read an article in which Ewald discussed using Darwinian theory to illuminate the origins of certain symptoms of infectious disease—things like fever, low iron counts, diarrhea. Ewald's approach struck a chord in Williams. Twenty-three years earlier he had written a paper proposing an evolutionary framework for senescence, or aging. "Way back in the 1950s I didn't worry about the practical aspects of senescence, the medical aspects," Williams notes. "I was pretty young then." Now, however, he sat up and took notice.

While Williams was discovering Ewald's work, Randolph Nesse was discovering Williams's. Nesse, a psychiatrist and a founder of the University of Michigan Evolution and Human Behavior Program, was exploring his own interest in the aging process, and he and Williams soon got together. "He had wanted to find a physician to work with on medical problems," says Nesse, "and I had long wanted to find an evolutionary biologist, so it was a very natural match for us." Their collaboration led to a 1991 article that most researchers say signaled the real birth of the field.

NESSE AND WILLIAMS DEFINE Darwinian medicine as the hunt for evolutionary explanations of vulnerabilities to disease. It can, as Ewald noted, be a way to interpret the body's defenses, to try to figure out, say, the reasons we feel

24

pain or get runny noses when we have a cold, and to determine what we should—or shouldn't—be doing about those defenses. For instance, Darwinian researchers like physiologist Matthew Kluger of the Lovelace Institute in Albuquerque now say that a moderate rise in body temperature is more than just a symptom of disease; it's an evolutionary adaptation the body uses to fight infection by making itself inhospitable to invading microbes. It would seem, then, that if you lower the fever, you may prolong the infection. Yet no one is ready to say whether we should toss out our aspirin bottles. "I would love to see a dozen proper studies of whether it's wise to bring fever down when someone has influenza," says Nesse. "It's never been done, and it's just astounding that it's never been done."

Diarrhea is another common symptom of disease, one that's sometimes the result of a pathogen's manipulating your body for its own good purposes, but it may also be a defense mechanism mounted by your body. Cholera bacteria, for example, once they invade the human body, induce diarrhea by producing toxins that make the intestine's cells leaky. The resultant diarrhea then both flushes competing beneficial bacteria from the gut and gives the cholera bacteria a ride into the world, so that they can find another hapless victim. In the case of cholera, then, it seems clear that stopping the diarrhea can only do good.

But the diarrhea that results from an invasion of shigella bacteria—which cause various forms of dysentery—seems to be more an intestinal defense than a bacterial offense. The infection causes the muscles surrounding the gut to contract more frequently, apparently in an attempt to flush out the bacteria as quickly as possible. Studies done more than a decade ago showed that using drugs like Lomotil to decrease the gut's contractions and cut down the diarrheal output actually prolong infection. On the other hand, the ingredients in over-the-counter preparations like Pepto Bismol, which don't affect how frequently the gut contracts, can be used to stem the diarrheal flow without prolonging infection.

Seattle biologist Margie Profet points to menstruation as another "symptom" that may be more properly viewed as an evolutionary defense. As Profet points out, there must be a good reason for the body to engage in such costly activities as shedding the uterine lining and letting blood flow away. That reason, she claims, is to rid the uterus of any organisms that might arrive with sperm in the seminal fluid. If an egg is fertilized, infection may be worth risking. But if there is no fertilized egg, says Profet, the body defends itself by ejecting the uterine cells, which might have been infected. Similarly, Profet has theorized that morning sickness during pregnancy causes the mother to avoid foods that might contain chemicals harmful to a developing fetus. If she's right, blocking that nausea with drugs could result in higher miscarriage rates or more birth defects.

DARWINIAN MEDICINE ISN'T simply about which symptoms to treat and which to ignore. It's a way to understand microbes—which, because they evolve so much more quickly than we do, will probably always beat us unless we figure out how to harness their evolutionary power for our own benefit. It's also a way to realize how disease-causing genes that persist in the population are often selected for, not against, in the long run.

Sickle-cell anemia is a classic case of how evolution tallies costs and benefits. Some years ago, researchers discovered that people with one copy of the sickle-cell gene are better able to resist the protozoans that cause malaria than are people with no copies of the gene. People with two copies of the gene may die, but in malaria-plagued regions such as tropical Africa, their numbers will be more than made up for by the offspring left by the disease-resistant kin.

Cystic fibrosis may also persist through such genetic logic. Animal studies indicate that individuals with just one copy of the cystic fibrosis gene may be more resistant to the effects of the cholera bacterium. As is the case with malaria and sickle-cell, cholera is much more prevalent than cystic fibrosis; since there are many more people with a single, resistance-conferring copy of the gene than with a disease-causing double dose, the gene is stably passed from generation to generation.

"I used to hunt saber-toothed tigers all the time, thousands of years ago. I got lots of exercise and all that sort of stuff. Now I sit in front of a computer and don't get exercise, so I've changed my body chemistry."

"With our power to do gene manipulations, there will be temptations to find genes that do things like cause aging, and get rid of them," says Nesse. "If we're sure about everything a gene does, that's fine. But an evolutionary approach cautions us not to go too fast, and to expect that every gene might well have some benefit as well as costs, and maybe some quite unrelated benefit."

Darwinian medicine can also help us understand the problems encountered in the New Age by a body designed for the Stone Age. As evolutionary psychologist Charles Crawford of Simon Fraser University in Burnaby, British Columbia, put it: "I used to hunt saber-toothed tigers all the time, thousands of years ago. I got lots of exercise and all that sort of stuff. Now I sit in front of a computer, and all I do is play with a mouse, and I don't get exercise. So I've changed my body biochemistry in all sorts of unknown ways, and it could affect me in all sorts of ways, and we have no idea what they are."

Radiologist Boyd Eaton of Emory University and his colleagues believe such biochemical changes are behind today's breast cancer epidemic. While it's impossible to study a Stone Ager's biochemistry, there are still groups of hunter-gatherers around—such as the San of Africa—who make admirable stand-ins. A foraging life-style, notes Eaton, also means a life-style in which menstruation begins later, the first child is born earlier, there are more children altogether, they are breast-fed for years rather than months, and menopause comes somewhat earlier. Overall, he says, American women today probably experience 3.5 times more menstrual cycles than our ancestors did 10,000 years ago. During each cycle a woman's body is flooded with the hormone estrogen, and breast cancer, as research has found, is very much estrogen related. The more frequently the breasts are exposed to the hormone, the greater the chance that a tumor will take seed.

Depending on which data you choose, women today are somewhere between 10 and 100 times more likely to be stricken with breast cancer than our ancestors were. Eaton's proposed solutions are pretty radical, but he hopes people will at least entertain them; they include delaying puberty with hormones and using hormones to create pseudopregnancies, which offer a woman the biochemical advantages of pregnancy at an early age without requiring her to bear a child.

In general, Darwinian medicine tells us that the organs and systems that make up our bodies result not from the pursuit of perfection but from millions of years of evolutionary compromises designed to get the greatest reproductive benefit at the lowest cost. We walk upright with a spine that evolved while we scampered on four limbs; balancing on two legs leaves our hands free, but we'll probably always suffer some back pain as well.

"What's really different is that up to now people have used evolutionary theory to try to explain why things work, why they're normal," explains Nesse. "The twist—and I don't know if it's simple or profound—is to say we're trying to understand the abnormal, the vulnerability to disease. We're trying to understand why natural selection has not made the body better, why natural selection has left the body with vulnerabilities. For every single disease, there is an answer to that question. And for very few of them is the answer very clear yet."

One reason those answers aren't yet clear is that few physicians or medical researchers have done much serious surveying from Darwin's viewpoint. In many cases, that's because evolutionary theories are hard to test. There's no way to watch human evolution in progress—

at best it works on a time scale involving hundreds of thousands of years. "Darwinian medicine is mostly a guessing game about how we think evolution worked in the past on humans, what it designed for us," say evolutionary biologist James Bull of the University of Texas at Austin. "It's almost impossible to test ideas that we evolved to respond to this or that kind of environment. You can make educated guesses, but no one's going to go out and do an experiment to show that yes, in fact humans will evolve this way under these environmental conditions."

Yet some say that these experiments can, should, and will be done. Howard Howland, a sensory physiologist at Cornell, is setting up just such an evolutionary experiment, hoping to interfere with the myopia, or nearsightedness, that afflicts a full quarter of all Americans. Myopia is thought to be the result of a delicate feedback loop that tries to keep images focused on the eye's retina. There's not much room for error: if the length of your eyeball is off by just a tenth of a millimeter, your vision will be blurry. Research has shown that when the eye perceives an image as fuzzy, it compensates by altering its length.

This loop obviously has a genetic component, notes Howland, but what drives it is the environment. During the Stone Age, when we were chasing buffalo in the field, the images we saw were usually sharp and clear. But with modern civilization came a lot of close work. When your eye focuses on something nearby, the lens has to bend, and since bending that lens is hard work, you do as little bending as you can get away with. That's why, whether you're conscious of it or not, near objects tend to be a bit blurry. "Blurry image?" says the eye. "Time to grow." And the more it grows, the fuzzier those buffalo get. Myopia seems to be a disease of industrial society.

To prevent that disease, Howland suggests going back to the Stone Age— or at least convincing people's eyes that that's where they are. If you give folks with normal vision glasses that make their eyes think they're looking at an object in the distance when they're really looking at one nearby, he says, you'll

avoid the whole feedback loop in the first place. "The military academies induct young men and women with twenty-twenty vision who then go through four years of college and are trained to fly an airplane or do some difficult visual task. But because they do so much reading, they come out the other end nearsighted, no longer eligible to do what they were hired to do," Howland notes. "I think these folks would very much like not to become nearsighted in the course of their studies." He hopes to be putting glasses on them within a year.

THE NUMBING PACE OF EVOlution is a much smaller problem for researchers interested in how the bugs that plague us do their dirty work. Bacteria are present in such large numbers (one person can carry around more pathogens than there are people on the planet) and evolve so quickly (a single bacterium can reproduce a million times in one human lifetime) that experiments we couldn't imagine in humans can be carried out in microbes in mere weeks. We might even, says Ewald, be able to use evolutionary theory to tame the human immunodeficiency virus.

"HIV is mutating so quickly that surely we're going to have plenty of sources of mutants that are mild as well as severe," he notes. "So now the question is, which of the variants will win?" As in the case of Ebola, he says, it will all come down to how well the virus manages to get from one person to another.

"If there's a great potential for sexual transmission to new partners, then the viruses that reproduce quickly will spread," Ewald says. "And since they're reproducing in a cell type that's critical for the well-being of the host—the helper T cell—then that cell type will be decimated, and the host is likely to suffer from it." On the other hand, if you lower the rate of transmission—through abstinence, monogamy, condom use—then the more severe strains might well die out before they have a chance to be passed very far. "The real question," says Ewald, "is, exactly how mild can you make this virus as a result of reducing the rate at which it could be transmitted to new partners, and how long will it take for this change to occur?" There are already strains of HIV in Senegal with such low virulence, he points out, that most people infected will die of old age. "We don't have all the answers. But I think we're going to be living with this virus for a long time, and if we have to live with it, let's live with a really mild virus instead of a severe virus."

Though condoms and monogamy are not a particularly radical treatment, that they might be used not only to stave off the virus but to tame it is a radical notion—and one that some researchers find suspect. "If it becomes too virulent, it will end up cutting off its own transmission by killing its host too quickly," notes James Bull. "But the speculation is that people transmit HIV primarily within one to five months of infection, when they spike a high level of virus in the blood. So with HIV, the main period of transmission occurs a few months into the infection, and yet the virulence—the death from it—occurs years later. The major stage of transmission is decoupled from the virulence." So unless the protective measures are carried out by everyone, all the time, we won't stop most instances of transmission; after all, most people don't even know they're infected when they pass the virus on.

But Ewald thinks these protective measures are worth a shot. After all, he says, pathogen taming has occurred in the past. The forms of dysentery we encounter in the United States are quite mild because our purified water supplies have cut off the main route of transmission for virulent strains of the bacteria.

Not only did hygienic changes reduce the number of cases, they selected for the milder shigella organisms, those that leave their victim well enough to get out and about. Diphtheria is another case in point. When the diphtheria vaccine was invented, it targeted only the most severe form of diphtheria toxin, though for economic rather than evolutionary reasons. Over the years, however, that choice has weeded out the most virulent strains of diphtheria, selecting for the ones that cause few or no symptoms. Today those weaker strains act like another level of vaccine to protect us against new, virulent strains.

"We did with diphtheria what we did with wolves. We took an organism that caused harm, and unknowingly, we domesticated it into an organism that protects us."

"You're doing to these organisms what we did to wolves," says Ewald. "Wolves were dangerous to us, we domesticated them into dogs, and then they helped us, they warned us against the wolves that were out there ready to take our babies. And by doing that, we've essentially turned what was a harmful organism into a helpful organism. That's the same thing we did with diphtheria; we took an organism that was causing harm, and without knowing it, we do-

mesticated it into an organism that is protecting us against harmful ones."

Putting together a new scientific discipline—and getting it recognized—is in itself an evolutionary process. Though Williams and Neese say there are hundreds of researchers working (whether they know it or not) within this newly built framework, they realize the field is still in its infancy. It may take some time before *Darwinian medicine* is a household term. Nesse tells how the editor of a prominent medical journal, when asked about the field, replied, "Darwinian medicine? I haven't heard of it, so it can't be very important."

But Darwinian medicine's critics don't deny the field's legitimacy; they point mostly to its lack of hard-and-fast answers, its lack of clear clinical guidelines. "I think this idea will eventually establish itself as a basic science for medicine, " answers Nesse. "What did people say, for instance, to the biochemists back in 1900 as they were playing out the Krebs cycle? People would say, 'So what does biochemistry really have to do with medicine? What can you cure now that you couldn't before you knew about the Krebs cycle?' And the biochemists could only say, 'Well, gee, we're not sure, but we know what we're doing is answering important scientific questions, and eventually this will be useful.' And I think exactly the same applies here."

Lori Oliwenstein, a former DISCOVER senior editor, is now a freelance journalist based in Los Angeles.

Chapter 3

Bittersweet Harvest

The Debate Over Genetically Modified Crops

Honor Hsin

In 1982 scientists on the 4th floor of the Monsanto Company U Building successfully introduced a foreign gene into a plant cell for the first time in history. These plants were genetically modified: they continued to express the new gene while exhibiting normal plant physiology and producing normal offspring. This breakthrough spawned the field of genetically modified (GM) crop production. Since the discovery, however, the international response to GM crops has been mixed. Along with the tremendous potential that lies vested in this technology, there are many risks and uncertainties involved as well. Arguments have centered on the health implications and environmental impact of cultivating GM crops and have raised disputes over national interests, global policy, and corporate agendas. Although there are many sides to this debate, discussions on GM crop regulation should be held within the context of scientific evidence, coupled with a careful weighing of present and future agricultural prospects.

Benefits and Costs

The possibility of environmental benefits first spurred the development of GM crops. The environmental issues at stake can be illustrated by one example of a potent genetic modification, the introduction of an endotoxin gene from *Bacillus thuringiensis* (Bt), a soil microorganism used for decades by organic growers as an insecticide, into soybeans, corn, and cotton. These GM crops promise to reduce the need to spray large amounts of chemicals into a field's ecosystem since the toxins are produced by the plants themselves. The Bt crops pose environmental risks, however, and could possibly harm other organisms. Bt corn was shown to harm monarch butterfly caterpillars in the laboratory, although later studies performed with more realistic farming conditions found this result conclusively only with Syngenta Company's Bt maize, which expressed up to 40 percent more toxin than other brands. Another pertinent environmental issue is the possible evolution of Bt resistance in pests. Since the Bt toxin expressed by the crops is ubiquitous in the field, there is positive selection for resistance against it, which would quickly make Bt's effect obsolete. Experimentation has begun, however, that involves regulating the percentage of Bt crops in a field so that a balance can be achieved between high yields and survival of Bt-sensitive pests. Although there are still multiple layers of ecosystem complexity that need to be considered, careful scientific research can begin to address these questions.

Another potential area of risk that needs to be analyzed is the effect of GM crops on human health. A possible consequence of Bt expression in crops is the development of allergic reactions in farmers since the toxin is more highly concentrated in the crops than in the field. Furthermore, the method used to insert foreign genes into GM crops always risks manipulation of unknown genes in the plant, resulting in unforeseen consequences. The effects of GM crops on humans therefore must be tested rigorously. Fortunately, no solid evidence yet exists for adverse physiological reactions to GM crops in humans, and some scientists argue that these same genetic-modification techniques are also currently being used in the development of pharmaceutical and industrial products.

A prevailing theme in the GM debate is that when discrepancies between scientific consensus and government policy result in unwanted consequences, the blame is often placed directly on GM crop technology itself. In 2000 about 300,000 acres of StarLink corn, a Bt crop produced by Aventis CropScience, were being cultivated in the United States. Since the US Environmental Protection Agency had declared its uncertainty over the allergenic potential of StarLink, the crops were grown with the understanding that they would be used solely as animal feed. Later that year news broke that StarLink corn had found its way into numerous taco food products around the world. This incident received wide press coverage and brought instant attention to the debate over GM crop safety. More at issue, though, were the United States' lax policies of GM crop approval and regulation. For nearly a decade, the US government made no distinction between GM crops and organically grown crops, and allergenicity safety tests were not mandatory. Only recently has the US Food and Drug Administration begun to reconsider its policies.

Canada is another leading producer of GM crops, with regulatory policies similar to those of the United States. Recent controversy surrounding Canada's cultivation of GM rapeseed, or canola, brought attention to another major environmental risk of GM crops. Unlike wheat and soybeans, which can self-pollinate to reproduce, the pollen of rapeseed plants spreads up to 800 meters beyond the field. There have been concerns in Ottawa over the government's refusal to reveal the location of ongoing GM wheat testing by Monsanto, resulting in fear of unwanted pollen spreading. This issue demonstrates one of the most potent risks of GM crops: uncontrolled breeding and the introduction of foreign genes into the natural ecosystem. An example of such an incident is Mexico's discovery of transgenic genes in non-GM strains of maize, although this result is still under scrutiny. More measures must be tested to restrain these possibilities. Current research on introducing the foreign genes into chloroplasts, which are only carried in the maternal line and not in pollen, offers a promising example.

Unfortunately, activist organizations rarely cite credible scientific evidence in their positions and have won much public sympathy by exploiting popular fears and misconceptions about genetic-engineering technology.

Europe's policy toward GM crops lies on the opposite end of the spectrum. In 1996 Europe approved the import of Monsanto's Roundup Ready soybeans and in 1997 authorized the cultivation of GM corn from Novartis. At around this time, however, there were rising concerns in Britain over BSE (bovine spongiform encephalopathy), or mad cow disease, which was thought to have killed more than two dozen people and cost the country the equivalent of billions of US dollars. The public was enraged over what it believed was a failure of government regulation, and in 1998 the European Commission voted to ban the import and cultivation of new GM crops. Besides the disappointment of private GM corporations like Monsanto, the United States claims to have lost US$600 million in corn exports to the

European Union. Recently, several European countries have considered lifting the ban contingent on the establishment of adequate labeling practices. The United States has complained to EU officials that labeling requirements discriminate against its agricultural exports, bringing the GM debate into the midst of a world trade dispute. In late January 2000, a tentative agreement was reached on the Montreal Biosafety Protocol in which the United States, Canada, Australia, Argentina, Uruguay, and Chile agreed to preliminary labeling of international exports and a precautionary principle allowing EU countries to reject imports if a scientific risk assessment of the imported crop is provided. This agreement, however, does not override decisions made by the World Trade Organization.

Corporate Control

The European public's anti-GM crop stance stems primarily from the success of environmental advocacy groups such as Greenpeace and Friends of the Earth. Numerous demonstrations have occurred throughout Britain, France, and other EU countries where GM crops have been uprooted and destroyed. Unfortunately, activist organizations rarely cite credible scientific evidence in their positions and have won much public sympathy by exploiting popular fears and misconceptions about genetic-engineering technology.

One issue they highlight that might prove significant, however, is the role of corporate interests in the GM-crop debate. A few years ago, Monsanto's attempt to acquire the "terminator" technology sparked tremendous controversy. This patent consisted of an elaborate genetically engineered control system designed to inhibit the generation of fertile seeds from crops. In essence, it was developed so that farmers would need to purchase new GM seeds each year, although arguments were raised that this technology could help prevent uncontrolled GM crop breeding. After much pressure from the nonprofit advocacy group Rural Advancement Foundation International, however, Monsanto announced in late 1999 that it would not market the "terminator" technology.

The "terminator" ordeal attracted so much attention because it placed Monsanto's corporate interest directly against the strongest argument in favor of genetic-engineering technology: potential cost savings and nutritional value of GM crops to developing countries. The UN Development Programme recently affirmed that GM crops could be the key to alleviating global hunger. Although the United Nations has expressed concern over precautionary testing of crops (through agencies like the World Health Organization), some contend that Western opposition to this technology ignores concerns of sub-Saharan and South Asian countries where malnutrition and poverty are widespread.

India is among those nations that could benefit from GM-crop technology. India's population has been growing by 1.8 percent annually; by 2025 India will need to produce 30 percent more grain per year to feed the twenty million new mouths added to its population. The need for higher food productivity is highlighted by incidents of poor farmers in Warangal and Punjab who have committed suicide when faced with devastated crops and huge debts on pesticides. The Indian government has approved several GM crops for commercial production, and testing has also commenced on transgenic cotton, rice, maize, tomato, and cauliflower, crops that would reduce the need for pesticides. A recent furor erupted over the discovery of around 11,000 hectares of illegal Bt cotton in Gujarat. The Gujarat administration responded immediately by ordering the fields stripped, the crops burned, and the seeds destroyed. There is still uncertainty over who will repay the farmers, who claim that Mahyco, a Monsanto subsidiary, is attempting to monopolize the distribution of Bt crops in India, and that the Indian government is also yielding to pressure from pesticide manufacturers. Corporate battles still abound in a nation where many farmers appear to be in need of agricultural change.

Feed the World

Many opponents of GM crops argue that the technology is not needed to help solve the problem of world hunger, with 800 million people who do not have enough to eat. They often argue that the world produces enough food to feed nine billion people while there are only six billion people today, implying that global hunger is simply a matter of distribution and not food productivity. Unfortunately, fixing the distribution problem is a complex issue. Purchasing power would need to increase in developing countries, coupled with increased food production in both developing and developed countries so that crops can be marketed at a price the underprivileged can afford. Since land for farming is limited, the remaining option for increasing crop productivity is to increase yield. While GM-crop technology is not the only method that can be used to achieve this end, it can contribute greatly toward it.

On Dr. Shiva's argument for supporting local knowledge in agricultural practices, Dr. Prakash argues that, from experience, "[local knowledge] is losing one third of your children before they hit the age of three. Is that the local knowledge that you want to keep reinforcing and keep perpetuating?"

Some consider GM crops part of a series of corporate attempts to control markets in developing countries and thus they brand GM technology another globalization "evil." Dr. Vandana Shiva of the Research Foundation for Science, Technology, and Ecology argues that globalization has pressured farmers in developing countries to grow monocultures—single-crop farming—instead of fostering sustainable agricultural diversity. Genetic engineering, in this view, is the next industrialization effort after chemical pesticides, and would also bear

no greater benefit than indigenous poly-cultural farming. The Food and Agricultural Organization of the United Nations also notes the leaning of research investment toward monocultures, spurred on by the profit potential of GM crops.

On the other hand, GM-crop technology serves to increase crop yield on land already in use for agricultural purposes, thereby preserving biodiversity in unused land. In the words of Dr. C. S. Prakash "using genetics helped [to] save so much valuable land from being under the plow." On Shiva's argument for supporting local knowledge in agricultural practices, Dr. Prakash argues that, from experience, "[local knowledge] is losing one third of your children before they hit the age of three. Is that the local knowledge that you want to keep reinforcing and keep perpetuating?"

Continuing along these lines and bringing GM technology in developing countries into the broader context of morality, leaders including Per Pinstrup-Andersen, director of the International Food Policy Research Institute, and Hassan Adamu, Nigeria's minister of agriculture, emphasize the importance of providing freedom of access, education, and choice in GM technology to the individual farmer himself. In Africa, for example, many local farmers have benefited from hybrid seeds obtained from multinational corporations. On a larger scale, however, Africa's agricultural production per unit area is among the lowest in the world, and great potential lies in utilizing GM crops to help combat pestilence and drought problems. On the issue of local knowledge, Dr. Florence Wambugu of the International Service for the Acquisition of Agribiotech Applications in Kenya (ISAAA) asserts that GM crops consist of "packaged technology in the seed" that can yield benefits without a change in local agricultural customs.

On another front of the world hunger debate, a promising benefit that GM-crop technology brings to developing countries is the introduction or enhancement of nutrients in crops. The first prod-

uct to address this was "golden rice," an engineered form of rice that expresses high levels of beta-carotene, a precursor of Vitamin A, which could be used to combat Vitamin A deficiency found in over 120 million children worldwide. Although many advocacy groups claim that the increased levels of Vitamin A from a golden rice diet are not high enough to fully meet recommended doses of Vitamin A, studies suggest that a less-than-full dose can still make a difference in an individual whose Vitamin A intake is already deficiently low. Currently the International Rice Research Institute is evaluating environmental and health concerns. After such tests are completed, however, there remains one final hurdle in the marketing process that advocates on both sides of the GM debate do agree on: multilateral access and sharing between public and private sectors. The International Undertaking on Plant Genetic Resources was established to foster such relationships for the world's key crops, but more discussions will have to take place on the intellectual-property rights of GM-crop patents.

Science First

Monsanto recently drafted a pledge of Five Commitments: Respect, Transparency, Dialogue, Sharing, and Benefits. These are qualities that all multinational organizations should bring to the debate over GM crops. In the meantime, the technology of genetic engineering has already emerged and bears promising potential. On the question of world hunger, GM crops are not the full solution, but they can play a part in one. There are possible risks which must be examined and compared to the risks associated with current agricultural conditions, and progress must not be sought too hastily. It is important to base considerations of the benefits and risks of GM crops on careful scientific research, rather than corporate interest or public fears.

HONOR HSIN, Staff Writer, *Harvard International Review*

Chapter 4

Black, White, Other

Racial categories are cultural constructs masquerading as biology

Jonathan Marks

While reading the Sunday edition of the *New York Times* one morning last February, my attention was drawn by an editorial inconsistency. The article I was reading was written by attorney Lani Guinier. (Guinier, you may remember, had been President Clinton's nominee to head the civil rights division at the Department of Justice in 1993. Her name was hastily withdrawn amid a blast of criticism over her views on political representation of minorities.) What had distracted me from the main point of the story was a photo caption that described Guinier as being "half-black." In the text of the article, Guinier had described herself simply as "black."

How can a person be black and half black at the same time? In algebraic terms, this would seem to describe a situation where $x = 1/2\ x$, to which the only solution is $x = 0$.

The inconsistency in the *Times* was trivial, but revealing. It encapsulated a longstanding problem in our use of racial categories—namely, a confusion between biological and cultural heredity. When Guinier is described as "half-black," that is a statement of biological ancestry, for one of her two parents is black. And when Guinier describes herself as black, she is using a cultural category, according to which one can either be black or white, but not both.

Race—as the term is commonly used—is inherited, although not in a strictly biological fashion. It is passed down according to a system of folk heredity, an all-or-nothing system that is different from the quantifiable heredity

of biology. But the incompatibility of the two notions of race is sometimes starkly evident—as when the state decides that racial differences are so important that interracial marriages must be regulated or outlawed entirely. Miscegenation laws in this country (which stayed on the books in many states through the 1960s) obliged the legal system to define who belonged in what category. The resulting formula stated that anyone with one-eighth or more black ancestry was a "negro." (A similar formula, defining Jews, was promulgated by the Germans in the Nuremberg Laws of the 1930s.)

Applying such formulas led to the biological absurdity that having one black great-grandparent was sufficient to define a person as black, but having seven white great grandparents was insufficient to define a person as white. Here, race and biology are demonstrably at odds. And the problem is not semantic but conceptual, for race is presented as a category of nature.

Human beings come in a wide variety of sizes, shapes, colors, and forms—or, because we are visually oriented primates, it certainly seems that way. We also come in larger packages called populations; and we are said to belong to even larger and more confusing units, which have long been known as races. The history of the study of human variation is to a large extent the pursuit of those human races—the attempt to identify the small number of fundamentally distinct kinds of people on earth.

This scientific goal stretches back two centuries, to Linnaeus, the father of bio-

logical systematics, who radically established *Homo sapiens* as one species within a group of animals he called Primates. Linnaeus's system of naming groups within groups logically implied further breakdown. He consequently sought to establish a number of subspecies within *Homo sapiens*. He identified five: four geographical species (from Europe, Asia, Africa, and America) and one grab-bag subspecies called *monstrosus*. This category was dropped by subsequent researchers (as was Linnaeus's use of criteria such as personality and dress to define his subspecies).

While Linnaeus was not the first to divide humans on the basis of the continents on which they lived, he had given the division a scientific stamp. But in attempting to determine the proper number of subspecies, the heirs of Linnaeus always seemed to find different answers, depending upon the criteria they applied. By the mid-twentieth century, scores of anthropologists—led by Harvard's Earnest Hooton—had expended enormous energy on the problem. But these scholars could not convince one another about the precise nature of the fundamental divisions of our species.

Part of the problem—as with the *Times's* identification of Lani Guinier—was that we humans have two constantly intersecting ways of thinking about the divisions among us. On the one hand, we like to think of "race"—as Linnaeus did—as an objective, biological category. In this sense, being a member of a race is supposed to be the equivalent of being a member of a species or of a phylum—except that race, on the analogy of subspecies, is an even narrower (and presumably more exclusive and precise) biological category.

The other kind of category into which we humans allocate ourselves—when we say "Serb" or "Hutu" or "Jew" or "Chicano" or "Republican" or "Red Sox fan"—is cultural. The label refers to little or nothing in the natural attributes of its members. These members may not live in the same region and may not even know many others like themselves. What they share is neither strictly nature nor strictly community. The groupings are constructions of human social history.

Membership in these *unbiological* groupings may mean the difference between life and death, for they are the categories that allow us to be identified (and accepted or vilified) socially. While membership in (or allegiance to) these categories may be assigned or adopted from birth, the differentia that mark members from nonmembers are symbolic and abstract; they serve to distinguish people who cannot be readily distinguished by nature. So important are these symbolic distinctions that some of the strongest animosities are often expressed between very similar-looking peoples. Obvious examples are Bosnian Serbs and Muslims, Irish and English, Huron and Iroquois.

Obvious natural variation is rarely so important as cultural difference. One simply does not hear of a slaughter of the short people at the hands of the tall, the glabrous at the hands of the hairy, the red-haired at the hands of the brown-haired. When we do encounter genocidal violence between different looking peoples, the two groups are invariably socially or culturally distinct as well. Indeed, the tragic frequency of hatred and genocidal violence between biologically indistinguishable peoples implies that biological differences such as skin color are not motivations but, rather, excuses. They allow nature to be invoked to reinforce group identities and antagonisms that would exist without these physical distinctions. But are there any truly "racial" biological distinctions to be found in our species?

Obviously, if you compare two people from different parts of the world (or whose ancestors came from different parts of the world), they will differ physically, but one cannot therefore define three or four or five basically different kinds of people, as a biological notion of race would imply. The anatomical properties that distinguish people—such as pigmentation, eye form, body build—are not clumped in discrete groups, but distributed along geographical gradients, as are nearly all the genetically determined variants detectable in the human gene pool.

These gradients are produced by three forces. Natural selection adapts populations to local circumstances (like climate) and thereby differentiates them from other populations. Genetic drift (random fluctuations in a gene pool) also differentiates populations from one another, but in non-adaptive ways. And gene flow (via intermarriage and other child-producing unions) acts to homogenize neighboring populations.

In practice, the operations of these forces are difficult to discern. A few features, such as body build and the graduated distribution of the sickle cell anemia gene in populations from western Africa, southern Asia, and the Mediterranean can be plausibly related to the effects of selection. Others, such as the graduated distribution of a small deletion in the mitochondrial DNA of some East Asian, Oceanic, and Native American peoples, or the degree of flatness of the face, seem unlikely to be the result of selection and are probably the results of random biohistorical factors. The cause of the distribution of most features, from nose breadth to blood group, is simply unclear.

The overall result of these forces is evident, however. As Johann Friedrich Blumenbach noted in 1775, "you see that all do so run into one another, and that one variety of mankind does so sensibly pass into the other, that you cannot mark out the limits between them." (Posturing as an heir to Linnaeus, he nonetheless attempted to do so.) But from humanity's gradations in appearance, no defined groupings resembling races readily emerge. The racial categories with which we have become so familiar are the result of our imposing arbitrary cultural boundaries in order to partition gradual biological variation.

Unlike graduated biological distinctions, culturally constructed categories are ultrasharp. One can be French or German, but not both; Tutsi or Hutu, but not both; Jew or Catholic, but not both; Bosnian Muslim or Serb, but not both; black or white, but not both. Traditionally, people of "mixed race" have been obliged to choose one and thereby identify themselves unambiguously to census takers and administrative bookkeepers—a practice that is now being widely called into question.

A scientific definition of race would require considerable homogeneity within each group, and reasonably discrete differences between groups, but three kinds of data militate against this view: First, the groups traditionally described as races are not at all homogeneous. Africans and Europeans, for instance, are each a collection of biologically diverse populations. Anthropologists of the 1920s widely recognized *three* European races: Nordic, Alpine, and Mediterranean. This implied that races could exist within races. American anthropologist Carleton Coon identified *ten* European races in 1939. With such protean use, the term race came to have little value in describing actual biological entities within *Homo sapiens.* The scholars were not only grappling with a broad north-south gradient in human appearance across Europe, they were trying to bring the data into line with their belief in profound and fundamental constitutional differences between groups of people.

But there simply isn't one European race to contrast with an African race, nor three, nor ten: the question (as scientists long posed it) fails to recognize the actual patterning of diversity in the human species. Fieldwork revealed, and genetics later quantified, the existence of far more biological diversity within any group than between groups. Fatter and thinner people exist everywhere, as do people with type O and type A blood. What generally varies from one population to the next is the *proportion* of people in these groups expressing the trait or gene. Hair color varies strikingly among Europeans and native Australians, but little among other peoples. To focus on discovering differences between presumptive races, when the vast majority of detectable variants do not help differentiate them, was thus to define a very narrow—if not largely illusory—problem in human biology. (The fact that Africans are biologically more diverse than Europeans, but have rarely been split into so many races, attests to the cultural basis of these categorizations.)

Second, differences between human groups are only evident when contrasting geographical extremes. Noting these extremes, biologists of an earlier era sought to identify representatives of "pure," primordial races presumably located in Norway, Senegal, and Thailand. At no time, however, was our species composed of a few populations within which everyone looked pretty much the same. Ever since some of our ancestors left Africa to spread out through the Old World, we humans have always lived in the "in-between" places. And human populations have also always been in genetic contact with one another. Indeed, for tens of thousands of years, humans have had trade networks; and where goods flow, so do genes. Consequently, we have no basis for considering *extreme* human forms the most pure, or most representative, of some ancient primordial populations. Instead, they represent populations adapted to the most disparate environments.

And third, between each presumptive "major" race are unclassifiable populations and people. Some populations of India, for example, are darkly pigmented (or "black"), have Europeanlike ("Caucasoid") facial features, but inhabit the continent of Asia (which should make them "Asian"). Americans might tend to ignore these "exceptions" to the racial categories, since immigrants to the United States from West Africa, Southeast Asia, and northwest Europe far outnumber those from India. The very existence of unclassifiable peoples undermines the idea that there are just three human biological groups in the Old World. Yet acknowledging the biological distinctiveness of such groups leads to a rapid proliferation of categories. What about Australians? Polynesians? The Ainu of Japan?

Categorizing people is important to any society. It is, at some basic psychological level, probably necessary to have group identity about who and what you are, in contrast to who and what you are not. The concept of race, however, specifically involves the recruitment of biology to validate those categories of self-identity.

Mice don't have to worry about that the way humans do. Consequently, classifying them into subspecies entails less of a responsibility for a scientist than classifying humans into sub-species does. And by the 1960s, most anthropologists realized they could not defend any classification of *Homo sapiens* into biological subspecies or races that could be considered reasonably objective. They therefore stopped doing it, and stopped identifying the endeavor as a central goal of the field. It was a biologically intractable problem—the old square-peg-in-a-round-hole enterprise; and people's lives, or welfares, could well depend on the ostensibly scientific pronouncement. Reflecting on the social history of the twentieth century, that was a burden anthropologists would no longer bear.

This conceptual divorce in anthropology—of cultural from biological phenomena was one of the most fundamental scientific revolutions of our time. And since it affected assumptions so rooted in our everyday experience, and resulted in conclusions so counterintuitive—like the idea that the earth goes around the sun, and not vice-versa—it has been widely underappreciated.

Kurt Vonnegut, in *Slaughterhouse Five*, describes what he remembered being taught about human variation: "At that time, they were teaching that there was absolutely no difference between anybody. They may be teaching that still." Of course there are biological differences between people, and between populations. The question is: How are those differences patterned? And the answer seems to be: Not racially. Populations are the only readily identifiable units of humans, and even they are fairly fluid, biologically similar to populations nearby, and biologically different from populations far away.

In other words, the message of contemporary anthropology is: You may group humans into a small number of races if you want to, but you are denied biology as a support for it.

New York-born Jonathan Marks earned an undergraduate degree in natural science at Johns Hopkins. After getting his Ph.D. in anthropology, Marks did a post-doc in genetics at the University of California at Davis and is now an associate professor of anthropology at Yale University. He is the coauthor, with Edward Staski, of the introductory textbook Evolutionary Anthropology *(San Diego: Harcourt, Brace Jovanovich, 1992). His new book,* Human Biodiversity: Genes, Race, and History *is published (1995) by Aldine de Gruyter.*

Chapter 5

The Evolution of Human Birth

The difficulties of childbirth have probably challenged humans and their ancestors for millions of years—which means that the modern custom of seeking assistance during delivery may have similarly ancient roots.

By Karen R. Rosenberg and Wenda R. Trevathan

GIVING BIRTH IN THE TREETOPS IS not the normal human way of doing things, but that is exactly what Sophia Pedro was forced to do during the height of the floods that ravaged southern Mozambique in March 2000. Pedro had survived for four days perched high above the raging floodwaters that killed more than 700 people in the region. The day after her delivery, television broadcasts and newspapers all over the world featured images of Pedro and her newborn child being plucked from the tree during a dramatic helicopter rescue.

Treetop delivery rooms are unusual for humans but not for other primate species. For millions of years, primates have secluded themselves in treetops or bushes to give birth. Human beings are the only primate species that regularly seeks assistance during labor and delivery. So when and why did our female ancestors abandon their unassisted and solitary habit? The answers lie in the difficult and risky nature of human birth.

Many women know from experience that pushing a baby through the birth canal is no easy task. It's the price we pay for our large brains and intelligence: humans have exceptionally big heads relative to the size of their bodies. Those who have delved deeper into the subject know that the opening in the human pelvis through which the baby must pass is limited in size by our upright posture. But only recently have anthropologists begun to realize that the complex twists and turns that human babies make as they travel through the birth canal have troubled humans and their ancestors for at least 100,000 years. Fossil clues also indicate that anatomy, not just our social nature, has led human mothers—in contrast to our closest primate relatives and almost all other mammals—to ask for help during childbirth. Indeed, this practice of seeking assistance may have been in place when the earliest members of our genus, *Homo*, emerged and may possibly date back to five million years ago, when our ancestors first began to walk upright on a regular basis.

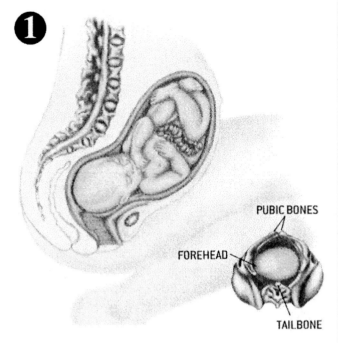

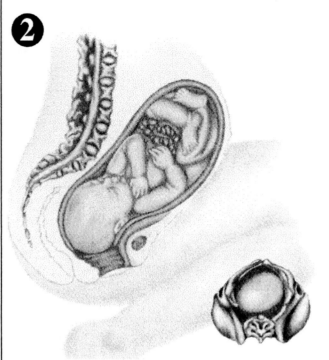

❶

❷

PUBIC BONES

FOREHEAD

TAILBONE

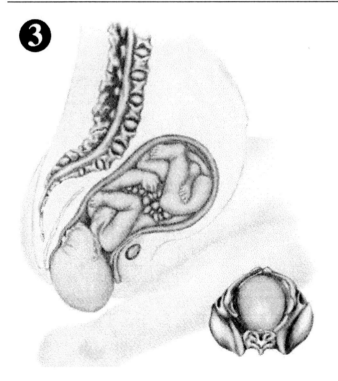

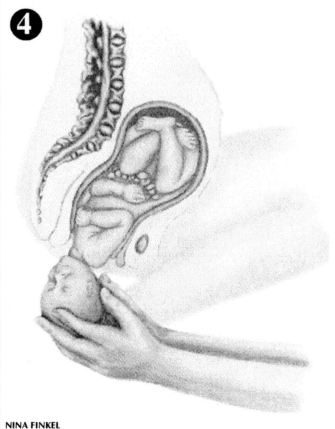

❸

❹

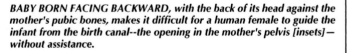

BABY BORN FACING BACKWARD, with the back of its head against the mother's pubic bones, makes it difficult for a human female to guide the infant from the birth canal--the opening in the mother's pelvis [insets]— without assistance.

NINA FINKEL

TIGHT SQUEEZE

To test our theory that the practice of assisted birth may have been around for millennia, we considered first what scientists know about the way a primate baby fits through the mother's birth canal. Viewed from above, the infant's head is basically an oval, longest from the forehead to the back of the head and narrowest from ear to ear. Conveniently, the birth canal—the bony opening in the pelvis through which the baby must travel to get from the uterus to the outside world—is also an oval shape. The challenge of birth for many primates is that the size of the infant's head is close to the size of that opening.

For humans, this tight squeeze is complicated by the birth canal's not being a constant shape in cross section. The entrance of the birth canal, where the baby begins its journey, is widest from side to side relative to the mother's body. Midway through, however, this orientation shifts 90 degrees, and the long axis of the oval extends from the front of the mother's body to her back. This means that the human infant must negotiate a series of turns as it works its way through the birth canal so that the two parts of its body with the largest dimensions—the head and the shoulders—are always aligned with the largest dimension of the birth canal.

Although humans are more closely related to apes genetically, monkeys may present a better model for birth in prehuman primates.

To understand the birth process from the mother's point of view, imagine you are about to give birth. The baby is most likely upside down, facing your side, when its head enters the birth canal. Midway through the canal, however, it must turn to face your back, and the back of its head is pressed against your pubic bones. At that time, its shoulders are oriented side to side. When the baby exits your body it is still facing backward, but it will turn its head slightly to the side. This rotation helps to turn the baby's shoulders so that they can also fit between your pubic bones and tailbone. To appreciate the close correspondence of the maternal and fetal dimensions, consider that the average pelvic opening in human females is 13 centimeters at its largest diameter and 10 centimeters at its smallest. The average infant head is 10 centimeters from front to back, and the shoulders are 12

centimeters across. This journey through a passageway of changing cross-sectional shape makes human birth difficult and risky for the vast majority of mothers and babies.

If we retreat far enough back along the family tree of human ancestors, we would eventually reach a point where birth was not so difficult. Although humans are more closely related to apes genetically, monkeys may present a better model for birth in prehuman primates. One line of reasoning to support this assertion is as follows: Of the primate fossils discovered from the time before the first known hominid, *Australopithecus*, one possible remote ancestor is *Proconsul*, a primate fossil dated to about 25 million years ago. This tailless creature probably looked like an ape, but its skeleton suggests that it moved more like a monkey. Its pelvis, too, was more monkeylike. The heads of modern monkey infants are typically about 98 percent the diameter of the mother's birth canal—a situation more comparable with that of humans than that of chimps, whose birth canals are relatively spacious.

Despite the monkey infant's tight squeeze, its entrance into the world is less challenging than that of a human baby. In contrast to the twisted birth canal of modern humans, monkeys' birth canals maintain the same cross-sectional shape from entrance to exist. The longest diameter of this oval shape is oriented front to back, and the broadest part of the oval is against the mother's back. A monkey infant enters the birth canal headfirst, with the broad back of its skull against the roomy back of the mother's pelvis and tailbone. That means the baby monkey emerges from the birth canal face forward—in other words, facing the same direction as the mother.

Firsthand observations of monkey deliveries have revealed a great advantage in babies' being born facing forward. Monkeys give birth squatting on their hind legs or crouching on all fours. As the infant is born, the mother reaches down to guide it out of the

birth canal and toward her nipples. In many cases, she also wipes mucus from the baby's mouth and nose to aid its breathing. Infants are strong enough at birth to take part in their own deliveries. Once their hands are free, they can grab their mother's body and pull themselves out.

Childbirth across Cultures

The complicated configuration of the human birth canal is such that laboring women and their babies benefit—by lower rates of mortality, injury and anxiety—from the assistance of others. This evolutionary reality helps to explain why attended birth is a near universal feature of human cultures. Individual women throughout history have given birth alone in certain circumstances, of course. But much more common is the attendance of familiar friends and relatives, most of whom are women. (Men may be variously forbidden, tolerated, welcomed or even required at birth.) In Western societies, where women usually give birth in the presence of strangers, recent research on birth practices has also shown that a doula—a person who provides social and emotional support to a woman in labor—reduces the rate of complications.

In many societies, a woman may not be recognized as an adult until she has had a baby. The preferred location of the delivery is often specified, as are the positions that the laboring women assume. The typical expectation in Western culture is that women should give birth lying flat on their backs on a bed, but in the rest of the world the most prevalent position for the delivery is upright—sitting, squatting or, in some cases, standing.

—*K. R. R. and W. R. T.*

If human babies were also born face forward, their mothers would have a much easier time. Instead the evolutionary modifications of the human pelvis that enabled hominids to walk upright necessitate that most infants exit the birth canal with the back of their heads against the pubic bones, facing in the opposing direction as the mother (in a position obstetricians call "occiput anterior"). For this reason, it is difficult for the laboring human mother—whether squatting, sitting, or lying on her back—to reach down and guide the baby as it emerges. This configuration also greatly inhibits the mother's ability to clear a breathing passage for the infant, to remove the umbilical cord from around its neck or even to lift the baby up to her breast. If she tries to accelerate the delivery by grabbing the baby and guiding it from the birth canal, she risks bending its back awkwardly against the natural curve of its spine. Pulling on a newborn at this angle risks injury to its spinal cord, nerves and muscles.

For contemporary humans, the response to these challenges is to seek assistance during labor and delivery. Whether a technology-oriented professional, a lay midwife or a family member who is familiar with the birth process, the assistant can help the human mother do all the things the monkey mother does by herself. The assistant can also compensate for the limited motor abilities of the relatively helpless human infant. The advantages of even simple forms of assistance have reduced maternal and infant mortality throughout history.

> … though rare exceptions do exist, assisted birth comes close to being a universal custom in human cultures.

ASSISTED BIRTH

Of course, our ancestors and even women today can and do give birth alone successfully. Many fictional accounts portray stalwart peasant women giving birth alone in the fields, perhaps most famously in the novel *The Good Earth*, by Pearl S. Buck. Such images give the impression that delivering babies is easy. But anthropologists who have studied childbirth in cultures around the world report that these perceptions are highly romanticized and that human birth is seldom easy and rarely unattended. Today virtually all women in all societies seek assistance at delivery. Even among the !Kung of southern Africa's Kalahari Desert—who are well known for viewing solitary birth as a cultural ideal—women do not usually manage to give birth alone until they have delivered several babies at which mothers, sisters or other women are present. So, though rare exceptions do exist, assisted birth comes close to being a universal custom in human cultures [*see box* "Childbirth across Cultures"].

Knowing this—and believing that this practice is driven by the difficulty and risk that accompany human birth—we began to think that midwifery is not unique to contemporary humans but instead has its roots deep in our ancestry. Our analysis of the birth process throughout human evolution has led us to suggest that the practice of midwifery might have appeared as early as five million years ago, when the advent of bipedalism first constricted the size and shape of the pelvis and birth canal.

A behavior pattern as complex as midwifery obviously does not fossilize, but pelvic bones do. The tight fit between the infant's head and the mother's birth canal in humans means that the mechanism of birth can be reconstructed if we know the relative sizes of each. Pelvic anatomy is now fairly well known from most time periods in the human fossil record, and we can estimate infant brain and skull size based on our extensive knowledge of adult skull sizes. (The delicate skulls of infants are not commonly found preserved until the point when humans began to bury their dead about 100,000 years ago.) Knowing the size and shape of the skulls and pelvises has also helped us and other researchers to understand whether infants were born facing forward or backward relative to their mothers—in turn revealing how challenging the birth might have been.

WALKING ON TWO LEGS

In modern humans, both bipedalism and enlarged brains constrain birth in important ways, but the first fundamental shift away from a nonhuman primate way of birth came about because of bipedalism alone. This unique way of walking appeared in early human ancestors of the genus *Australopithecus* about four million years ago [see "Evolution of Human Walking," by C. Owen Lovejoy; SCIENTIFIC AMERICAN, November 1988]. Despite their upright posture, australopithecines typically stood no more than four feet tall, and their brains were not much bigger than those of living chimpanzees. Recent evidence has called into question which of the several australopithecine species were part of the lineage that led to *Homo*. Understanding the way any of them gave birth is still important, however, because walking on two legs would have constricted the maximum size of the pelvis and birth canal in similar ways among related species.

The anatomy of the female pelvis from this time period is well known from two complete fossils. Anthropologists unearthed the first (known as Sts 14 and presumed to be 2.5 million years old) in Sterkfontein, a site in the Transvaal region of South Africa. The second is best known as Lucy, a fossil discovered in the Hadar region of Ethiopia and dated at just over three million years old. Based on these specimens and on estimates of newborns' head size, C. Owen Lovejoy of Kent State University and Robert G. Tague of Louisiana State University concluded in the mid-1980s that birth in early hominids was unlike that known for any living species of primate.

The shape of the australopithecine birth canal is a flattened oval with the greatest dimension from side to side at both the entrance and exit. This shape appears to require a birth pattern different from that of monkeys, apes or modern humans. The head would not have rotated within the birth canal, but we think that in order for the shoulders to fit through, the baby might have had to turn its head once it emerged. In other words, if the baby's head entered the birth canal facing the side of the mother's body, its shoulders would have been oriented in a line from the mother's belly to her back. This starting position would have meant that the shoulders probably also had to turn sideways to squeeze through the birth canal.

… changes in pelvic anatomy, accompanied by assisted birth, may have allowed the dramatic increase in human brain size that took place from two million to 100,000 years ago.

This simple rotation could have introduced a kind of difficulty in australopithecine deliveries that no other known primate species had ever experienced. Depending on which way the baby's shoulders turned, its head could have exited the birth canal facing either forward or backward relative to the mother. Because the australopithecine birth canal is a symmetrical opening of unchanging shape, the baby could have just as easily turned its shoulders toward the front or back of its body, giving it about a 50-50 chance of emerging in the easier, face-forward position. If the infant were born facing backward, the australopithecine mother—like modern human mothers—may well have benefited from some kind of assistance.

GROWING BIGGER BRAINS
If bipedalism alone did not introduce into the process of childbirth enough difficulty for mothers to benefit from assistance, then the expanding size of the hominid brain certainly did. The most significant

expansion in adult and infant brain size evolved subsequent to the australopithecines, particularly in the genus *Homo*. Fossil remains of the pelvis of early *Homo* are quite rare, and the best-preserved specimen, the 1.5-million-year-old Nariokotome fossil from Kenya, is an adolescent often referred to as Turkana Boy. Researchers have estimated that the boy's adult relatives probably had brains about twice as large as those of australopithecines but still only two thirds the size of modern human brains.

By reconstructing the shape of the boy's pelvis from fragments, Christopher B. Ruff of Johns Hopkins University and Alan Walker of Pennsylvania State University have estimated what he would have looked like had he reached adulthood. Using predictable differences between male and female pelvises in more recent hominid species, they could also infer what a female of that species would have looked like and could estimate the shape of the birth canal. That shape turns out to be a flattened oval similar to that of the australopithecines. Based on these reconstructions, the researchers determined that Turkana Boy's kin probably had a birth mechanism like that seen in australopithecines.

In recent years, scientists have been testing an important hypothesis that follows from Ruff and Walker's assertion: the pelvic anatomy of early *Homo* may have limited the growth of the human brain until the evolutionary point at which the birth canal expanded enough to allow a larger infant head to pass. This assertion implies that bigger brains and roomier pelvises were linked from an evolutionary perspective. Individuals who displayed both characteristics were more successful at giving birth to offspring who survived to pass on the traits. These changes in pelvic anatomy, accompanied by assisted birth, may have allowed the dramatic increase in human brain size that took place from two million to 100,000 years ago.

Fossils that span the past 300,000 years of human evolution support the connection between the expansion of

brain size and changes in pelvic anatomy. In the past 20 years, scientists have uncovered three pelvic fossils of archaic *Homo sapiens:* a male from Sima de los Huesso in Sierra Atapuerca, Spain (more than 200,000 years old); a female from Jinniushan, China (280,000 years old); and the male Kebara Neandertal—which is also an archaic *H. sapiens*—from Israel (about 60,000 years old). These specimens all have the twisted pelvic openings characteristic of modern humans, which suggests that their large-brained babies would most likely have had to rotate the head and shoulders within the birth canal and would thus have emerged facing away from the mother—a major challenge that human mothers face in delivering their babies safely.

The triple challenge of big-brained infants, a pelvis designed for walking upright, and a rotational delivery in which the baby emerges facing backward is not merely a contemporary circumstance. For this reason, we suggest that natural selection long ago favored the behavior of seeking assistance during birth because such help compensated for these difficulties. Mothers probably did not seek assistance solely because they predicted the risk that childbirth poses, however. Pain, fear and anxiety more likely drove their desire for companionship and security.

Psychiatrists have argued that natural selection might have favored such emotions—also common during illness and injury—because they led individuals who experienced them to seek the protection of companions, which would have given them a better chance of surviving [see "Evolution and the Origins of Disease," by Randolph M. Nesse and George C. Williams; SCIENTIFIC AMERICAN, November 1998]. The offspring of the survivors would then also have an enhanced tendency to experience such emotions during times of pain or disease. Taking into consideration the evolutionary advantage that fear and anxiety impart, it is no surprise that women commonly experience these emotions during labor and delivery.

Modern women giving birth have a dual evolutionary legacy: the need for physical as well as emotional support. When Sophia Pedro gave birth in a tree surrounded by raging floodwaters, she may have had both kinds of assistance. In an interview several months after her helicopter rescue, she told reporters that her mother-in-law, who was also in the tree, helped her during delivery. Desire for this kind of support, it appears, may well be as ancient as humanity itself.

MORE TO EXPLORE

Human Birth: An Evolutionary Perspective. Wenda R. Trevathan. Aldine de Gruyter, 1982.

Birth as an American Rite of Passage. Robbie Davis-Floyd. University of California Press, 1993.

Bipedalism and Human Birth: The Obstetrical Dilemma Revisited. Karen R. Rosenberg and Wenda R. Trevathan in *Evolutionary Anthropology*, Vol. 4, No. 5, pages 161–168; 1996.

On Fertile Ground: A Natural History of Human Reproduction. Peter T. Ellison. Harvard University Press, 2001.

KAREN R. ROSENBERG and *WENDA R. TREVATHAN* bring different perspectives to the study of human birth. Rosenberg, a paleo-anthropologist at the University of Delaware, specializes in pelvic morphology and has studied hominid fossils from Europe, Israel, China and South Africa. About 15 years ago she began studying the pelvis as a way to reconstruct the evolution of the birth process. That's when she met Trevathan, a biological anthropologist at New Mexico State University, whose particular interests include childbirth, maternal behavior, sexuality, menopause and evolutionary medicine. Both authors have experienced birth firsthand: Rosenberg has two daughters, and Trevathan is trained as a midwife.

Chapter 6

Karisoke Field Impressions

Dian Fossey

MY KNOWLEDGE OF KABARA'S FATE, as gained from the air, made the research at Karisoke seem more imperative than ever. However, even the prospect of unknown gorillas to identify and habituate did not ease my mind about the destiny of the Kabara population. At Kabara I had studied three groups totaling 50 individuals. During the first year at Karisoke I concentrated observations on four main groups that totaled 51 individuals living within the 9 1/2 square-mile study area around camp. These groups, identified by number according to the order in which contacted, were Groups 4, 5, 8, and 9. Other groups encountered were considered fringe groups whose ranges either abutted or overlapped those of the main study groups, or were totally unhabituated groups met during census work on other mountains.

Since I tried to distribute observation hours evenly among the four main study groups, lapses of several days could occur between successive contacts with any one of them. My tracking ability of necessity improved, because the trails were older and longer than if each group

had been tracked daily, and the Rwandese on my staff were yet to become skilled trackers.

A good six months were to pass before the men felt confident enough to go out into the forest and track by themselves. Even then, they clearly preferred not going more than an hour from camp and were reluctant to follow trails older than two or three days because of the distances involved. With old trails two trackers, rather than one, went out together. Much of the terrain was still unfamiliar to them and they retained a natural apprehension of possible encounters with wildlife or poachers.

Teaching Rwandese how to track was far easier than instructing the students who eventually came to Karisoke. The locals' senses, especially their eyesight, were more acute. When training anyone, I always led the way for a couple of days, explaining the factors that determined the route taken. Sometimes I purposely strayed from an actual gorilla trail (occasionally unintentionally) to see how long it would take those behind me to realize the error. Another beneficial teaching ruse was furtively to press a series of my own knuckleprints along a section of damp earth going in the opposite direction to the knuckleprints of the gorillas being followed. How Sanwekwe would have loved this bit of chicanery! Those being trained would excitedly discover my knuckleprints and confidently follow them only to find no gorilla spoor ahead. This method proved to be the best way to teach people not to blunder about when on difficult trails — trails on grassy meadows or rocky slopes in particular, where even one bootprint can destroy a vital tracking clue.

Following gorilla track in thick herbaceous foliage is in fact child's play. Most vegetation bends in the direction of a group's travel, knuckleprints may be found impressed upon intermittent dirt patches or trails, and chains of gorilla dung deposits provide other clues as to the direction of the animals' passage. The individuals of a calmly moving group do not travel one after another. There may be nearly as many trails as group members, so I attempt always to follow the most central trail. Numerous cul-de-sacs occur wherever individuals depart from the main route to go off and feed by themselves. I learned eventually that the false leads could be identified by the presence of two layers of foliage. The top one is bent in the direction of the group's travel and the lower is bent in the opposite direction where an individual has gone off on its own before returning to follow the group.

In extremely dense, tall foliage, much circuitous tracking time could be saved by looking ahead of a group's trail for signs of disturbance of vegetation or of branches in distant trees where gorillas have climbed to feed. This technique was especially helpful in the saddle areas, where gorilla spoor could be nearly eradicated by passage of elephant or large herds of buffalo. The ground signs that might survive between the miniature craters left by the elephants' feet are the gorillas' typical trilocular dung deposits or their feeding remnants, such as the unmistakable peelings of thistle and celery stalks. Often, gorilla

trail merges briefly with or zigzags in and out of buffalo trail. Whenever this happens and visual clues are obscured by vegetation I feel with my fingertips for the deep imprints left by the cloven hooves of the buffalo to realize that I am on the wrong path. Because gorillas always seek fresh untrampled vegetation for feeding purposes, they seldom travel along buffalo trails for any distance.

Unfortunately, the reverse is not true. Characteristically bovine in nature, buffalo are very trail-oriented, particularly in thick vegetation. Upon encountering gorilla trails, they often follow them like so many cows heading for the barn. On several occasions, without intention I found myself following gorillas who were in turn being followed by buffalo. Twice the gorillas, either in vexation or perhaps with a sense of joie-de-vivre, turned and charged directly toward the buffalo, which speedily turned tail and retreated unknowingly toward me. In retrospect, the subsequent confrontations had all the comical ingredients of a Laurel and Hardy movie. I had the option of climbing any available tree or diving headfirst into vegetation — too often nettles—that fringed the trail of the oncoming herd. I was always more than willing to let buffalo have the right-of-way. This is one of the first rules any person must learn when working in the domain of wild animals and is one that some learn the hard way.

Tracking is an enjoyable challenge, though there were times when trackers became convinced that their four-legged quarry had sprouted wings, so faint were the clues. This was especially true when trying to follow the trail of a lone silverback gorilla rather than a group, trails more than a week old, trails crossing relatively barren regions such as meadows or lava rockslides, and trails traversed by ungulates sharing the gorillas' terrain.

One morning along the trail of a lone silverback I was belly-crawling under a long dank tunnel roofed by a fallen *Hagenia* tree and sided by dense vines. With relief I saw a sunlit opening about fifteen feet ahead and wormed toward it enthusiastically while dragging my knapsack behind me. Upon reaching it I grabbed on to what appeared to be the base of a sapling in order to pull myself out of the gloomy tunnel confines. The intended support not only hauled me out of the tunnel but dragged me through several feet of nettles before I had the sense to let go of the left leg of a very surprised buffalo. The odoriferous deposits of his justifiable fright took several days to wash out of my hair and clothing. Much can be gained by crawling, rather than walking, along gorilla trail, a fact I discovered one day by accident. Traces of a silverback's pungent body odor, resembling human nondeodorized sweat smell, permeated vegetation the gorilla had traveled through some twenty-four hours previously. Had I been walking after the lone silverback that day rather than crawling, I never would have realized the importance of olfactory clues existing at ground level. There are two types of sweat glands existing in gorilla skin. The axillary region of the adult male contains four to seven layers of large apocrine glands responsible for the powerful fear odor of the silverback, an odor only weakly transmitted by the adult female. The palms and soles of males and females contain apocrine glands and a high concentration of

eccrine glands that have an important lubrication function. Both types of gland would appear to be evolutionary adaptations for terrestrial travel and olfactory communication, particularly for adult male gorillas.

The most outstanding odor found along fresh gorilla trail emanates from the dung deposits. Healthy gorillas leave chains of dung lobes similar in texture and smell to those of horses. When gorillas travel at an unhurried pace, the three-lobed sections may be deposited in a chain with the lobes attached to one another by strands of fibrous vegetation. If the animals have been feeding on fruit such as wild blackberries (*Rubus runssorensis*) or the plum-sized *Pygeum africanum*, the seeds, or even the whole fruit, can be found intact in the dung and can provide clues as to where the group had been ranging. The relative age of dung can be determined by the number of flies swarming around it, as well as the amount of eggs the flies have laid on the dung's surface. Countless hundreds of small white eggs are laid within minutes following defecation and begin hatching within eight to twelve hours, the variation dependent on the weather. Weather always has to be considered when determining the age of a trail. Sunny warm days make fresh spoor, such as dung or foliage discards, appear old by drying them out after only a few hours of exposure, whereas rain or heavy mist have exactly the opposite effect. I found it helpful during the early days of the study to return to camp with fresh dung specimens and vegetation discards and then record their aging process under various weather conditions. Repetition of this simple procedure soon improved my ability to gauge the age of trails accurately. To evaluate distances more precisely I set up stakes outside the tent, 50 to 250 feet apart, so that actual rather than approximate measures became familiar.

The dung of lactating females is often covered with a whitish sheath, possibly a result of the tendency gorilla mothers have to eat the feces of their offspring during the infant's first four to six months of life. Diarrhetic dung, either with or without a mucoid sheath or flecks of blood, when deposited by only one individual of a group, often signifies that the individual is ill. When numerous animals of a group leave diarrhetic dung along a trail, it is an indication that the gorillas have been alarmed by another group or, more likely, by poachers. These types of deposits are always found on flee trails created when a group has rapidly run, almost single file, from a potential threat. The time I spend following a flee trail seems horridly prolonged because of growing apprehensions about what may be found at the end of it.

Occasionally, various groups acquire a communal cestode parasite (*Anoplocephala gorillae*), an infection that could not be correlated with either seasonal or range patterns. Large flatworm segments, about 1 inch long, are most frequently found in feces deposited in night nests and, when examined early in the morning, the dung contents of the nests seem virtually alive, crawling with activity.

All age and sex classes of gorillas have been observed eating their own dung and, to a lesser extent, that of other gorillas. Coprophagy is most likely to occur after prolonged day-resting periods during the rainy season, when both feeding and travel time are minimized. The animals simply shift their buttocks slightly to catch the dung lobe in one hand before it contacts the earth. They then bite into the lobe and while chewing smack their lips with apparent relish. The eating of excrement occurs among most vertebrates, including humans, who have certain nutritional deficiencies. Among gorillas coprophagy is thought to have possible dietary functions because it may allow vitamins, particularly Vitamin B_{12}, synthesized in the hind gut, to be assimilated in the foregut. Since the activity is usually observed during periods of cold wet weather, I am inclined to relate the "meals" to instant warmed TV dinners!

Between age and sex classes dung sizes vary tremendously, ranging from around 3 inches for silverbacks, to 3/8 - 1 inch for infants. Analyzing the dung contents of the night nests makes it possible to determine the composition of fringe or census groups, and is also a reliable means of learning if births or transfers have occurred within study groups. (Most births occur during the night and night nests contain nearly half of the dung deposited by an individual over a twenty-four-hour period.)

Gorillas are diurnal and build their nests in different locations each evening. Ninety-eight percent of gorillas' night nests are built from nonfood vegetation, since food items such as thistles, nettles, and celery are not suitable nesting material. Adult night nests are sturdy, compact structures, sometimes resembling oval, leafy bathtubs made from bulky plants such as Lobelia (*Lobelia giberroa*) and Senecio (*Senecio erici-rosenii*). Construction is concentrated on the rim of the nest, which is composed of multiple bent stalks, the leafy ends of which are tucked around and under the animal's body for a more "cushiony" central bottom. Nests can be built in trees as well as on the ground, but because of adult gorillas' great weight nests are more commonly found on the ground. Favored nesting locations during the rainy season are in the sheltered hollows of tree trunks and nests may be made only of moss or loose soil. These types of nests not only offer protection from the elements but also provide early morning snacks in the form of decayed tree bark and roots.

Nests built by immatures are often only flimsy clusters of leaves until practice enables the construction of a solid, serviceable nest. The youngest animal observed consistently building and sleeping within his own night nest was thirty-four months old. Ordinarily a youngster remains sleeping in the mother's nest until the female again gives birth.

Some degree of predetermination is shown in the choice of night-nesting sites when gorillas are in areas adjacent to the park boundaries or near routes frequently used by poachers. The animals then tend to select knolls or open slopes offering good vantage points from which to view the surrounding terrain. This same type of choice also occurs when other gorilla groups are nearby. Less selectivity is demonstrated in the choice of day-nesting sites, although on sunny days areas with optimal sun exposure are far more frequently used than shaded or heavily treed regions.

For many years the slopes immediately behind camp were a part of the ranges of Groups 4 and 5. On dozens of occasions I found that the females and younger group members built their night nests about one hundred feet up on the slope near camp, whereas the silverbacks nested at the hill's base. This arrangement made it almost impossible for anyone to approach the gorillas undetected. When either Group 4 or 5 nested behind camp, I would approach them cautiously the following dawn in the hope of observing the animals before they awoke. Without fail I would almost step on a sleeping silverback sentry obscured in the tall foliage at the base of the slope. It was difficult to know which of us was the more shocked as the rudely awakened animal instantly jumped to his feet screaming in alarm before, running uphill to "defend" his family, all now thoroughly awakened.

Vestiges of tree nests last as long as four years, far longer than those constructed in ground foliage, which last some five months, depending upon weather conditions or location. Clusters of night nests made from tall lobelia plants often yield interesting information concerning the frequency and length of gorillas' use of certain areas. Lobelias continue to grow in height even after their top leafy crowns have been broken off for nests. I have estimated that these plants grow about two or three inches a year. An area containing circles of lobelia stalks, some 10 feet tall, suggests that nesting sites were perhaps built there about thirty years earlier.

There is some speculation that night nests either offer protection from the weather or may be an innate activity remaining from gorillas ancestral tree-living prototypes. Both points of view are plausible. I have observed numerous zoo gorillas born in captivity who apparently innately, rather than imitatively, utilized any remotely suitable object to shape around or under their bodies, much in the same manner that free-living gorillas use vegetation. Once I watched a lady's large straw hat blow into a zoo enclosure and be immediately retrieved by an adult female gorilla. The animal painstakingly ripped the hat into shreds to "build" a flimsy nest around herself while staunchly defending her nesting material against the other individuals in the cage.

Normally gorilla groups spend about 40 percent of their days resting, 30 percent feeding, and 30 percent traveling or travel-feeding — times when both movement and eating occur simultaneously. Around the Karisoke Research Centre's study area of 9 1/2 square miles there are seven major vegetation zones, each attractive to gorillas at various times of the year according to weather and season.

The saddle zone is relatively flat terrain lying between the three westerly volcanoes (Mts. Visoke, Karisimbi, and Mikeno) and interspersed with hills and ridges no more than 98 feet high. The saddle contains the richest variety of vines and herbaceous ground foliage, in addition to having the highest frequency of *Hagenia* and *Hypericum* trees.

The *Vernonia* zone is found in small areas of the saddle as well as on the lower slopes of Visoke. The flowers, bark, and pulp of *Vernonia* trees are favored gorilla food. This tree species is so frequently selected for nesting and play activities that it is becoming increasingly rare in some areas of previous abundance.

The nettle zone is found in small sections of the saddle and on the lower Visoke slopes, but the main nettle area lies at the western base of Visoke in a dense belt varying in width from one to two fifths of a mile.

The bamboo zone is a limited region found primarily along the eastern boundary of the park and is responsible for seasonal movements of Group 5. Only a few isolated clumps of bamboo grow in the saddle of Group 4's range, but when the bamboo begins shooting, the group leaves the mountain slopes and unerringly travels straight to the bamboo clumps, indicating their keen recollection of both season and location of food sources.

The brush zone is found mainly along ridges of Visoke's slopes and, to a lesser extent, on hills in the saddle. I consider it a separate zone because it contains a high density of favored fruit shrubs and trees, such as blackberry and *Pygeum*, and rarer trees and brush whose bark is avidly sought by the gorillas.

The giant lobelia zone is found 11,480 to 12,465 feet on Visoke's upper slopes. This area is frequented by gorillas during drier months when the high mountain vegetation retains moisture from nightly mists. For this reason succulence can be obtained from the brush, trees, and foliage characteristic of the region.

The Afro-alpine zone encompasses the highest portion of the mountain summits and consists mainly of open grass or lichen-covered meadows. This is a sparse, bleak area containing little gorilla vegetation.

Gorillas travel more rapidly in areas where food resources are limited, and also when they are undertaking "exploratory sallies" — treks into unfamiliar terrain. Such ventures appear to be the means by which either a lone silverback or a group can expand its saddlezone range. Range expansion into the saddle avoids extensive overlapping with other groups, as was the case on Visoke's slopes in the late 1960s. Often when tracking gorillas on these long crosscountry treks, I whimsically pictured the silverbacks urging on their group members by saying, "Okay guys, let's just see what's on the other side of this next little hill!" Frequently the animals ended up in totally unsuitable gorilla habitat and had to traverse back and forth in order to find small oases containing food vegetation before renewing their quest for satisfactory terrain. Sometimes their travel routes were so erratic that I became certain, especially on foggy days when the mountaintops were hidden from view, that the animals were either lost or extremely disoriented.

Acquisition of new range area is more often achieved within the saddle zone than on the slopes, because the saddle's expansive land surface offers a greater abundance and variety of preferred vegetation. Gorillas feed upon some fifty-eight plant species from the seven zones in the study area. Leaves, shoots, and stems form about 86 percent of the diet and fruits only 2 percent. Dung, dirt, bark, roots, grubs, and snails are also eaten, but to a far lesser extent than foliage. The most common herbaceous plants consumed are thistles, nettles, and celery — which could grow up to eight feet. The scraggly *Galium* vine forms the bulk of the gorillas' diet, most likely because it, unlike other vegetation, grows at nearly all levels of the forest from amid thick ground foliage to the tops of tree branches, where it is more easily obtained by agile immatures than by adults.

There is the possibility that gorillas improve their habitat within tall herbaceous vegetation both in the saddle and on the mountain slopes. Cattle and buffalo, with their corneous, sharp hooves, sever plant stems underfoot; but gorillas' hands and feet, with their padded soles, press herbaceous foliage into the earth, and thereby cause more rapid regeneration because of the increased number of shoots sprouting from the nodes of the semiburied stems. By marking off small plots of foliage traversed only by gorillas, some plots frequented only by bovines, and the remaining used by neither, I was able to see, within a six-week period, that the sections covered by gorillas had a far denser growth of vegetation, particularly nettles and thistles.

Competition over food resources is seldom observed among gorillas unless the sources of favored food are restricted by short seasonal growth or clumped in small areas. One such example is the *Pygeum* fruit tree that grows oaklike about 60 feet tall and is found only on a few mountain ridges. Because of the relative scarcity of the trees and their brief fruiting season — only two to three months a year — the ridges that support them attract concentrations of gorilla groups all at one time. It is a spectacular sight to watch massive silverbacks gingerly climbing to the highest branches in search of the small delicacies. Because of status, silverbacks have first culling choice while animals of lesser rank wait their turns at the bottom until the patriarchs descend. After gathering mouthfuls and handfuls of the fruit, the gorillas skillfully maneuver themselves to the nearest sturdy perch upon which to sit and enjoy their meager harvest.

Another scarce and keenly sought food is related to mistletoe. At altitudes around 10,000 feet it grows on spindly trees such as *Hypericum*. Thus immature animals are able to collect the leafy flowered stalks more proficiently than weighty adults who frequently have to sit under trees waiting for *Lorantbus* tidbits to fall their way. Youngsters who make the mistake of painstakingly descending to the forest floor to eat their collection more comfortably are usually bothered by pilfering adults who have no trouble "bullying" the young out of their acquisitions.

Still another special food is bracket fungus (*Ganoderma applanatum*), a parasitical tree growth resembling a large solidified mushroom. The shelflike projection is difficult to break free from a tree, so younger animals often have to wrap their arms and legs awkwardly around a trunk and content themselves by only gnawing at the delicacy. Older animals who succeed in breaking the fungus loose have been observed carrying it several hundred feet from its source, all the while guarding it possessively from more dominant individuals' attempts to take it away. Both the scarcity of the fungus and the gorillas' liking of it cause many intragroup squabbles, a number of which are settled by the silverback, who simply takes the item of contention for himself.

Group disputes also arise when restricted feeding sites containing prized foods create crowded conditions. The most common example occurs whenever an entire group seeks access to limited bamboo patches such as are found in the saddle zone. This also happens in the dry months when gorillas go on soil-eating binges on Visoke's ridges, where some earth is particularly rich in calcium and potassium. For many years one cavernous "dig" was favored by Group 5. The ridge supporting numerous trees had been so dug out by the gorillas that the tree roots formed exposed gnarled supports for the vast caves created by the animals' repeated soil digging.

Upon approaching this region, the leader of Group 5 went first as a matter of course, while other group members resigned themselves to waiting outside the favored cave. It was eerie to watch the huge silverback magically disappear beneath a web of tree roots into total blackness. When he emerged, covered with the sandy crumbs of his feast, he moved off, leaving the cavern to the other group members. In order of rank, they disappeared into its depths. Their subsequent screams and pig-grunts reflected the overcrowded conditions.

Group 4 chose their dirt mainly from sandy slides. Year after year the slides also attracted swallows to bathe and nest in the loose dirt. Much like Group 5, Group 4 headed for these barren areas during dry seasons to scoop up the soil with their hands and ingest handfuls of dirt. Even after hours of observation at these spots, I never saw gorillas attempt to catch adult swallows, their young, or their eggs.

Since gorillas mainly eat vegetation, food preparation involves manual and oral dexterity, attributes with which gorillas are well endowed. Perhaps for this reason gorillas have not yet been observed fashioning objects within their environment as tools. By contrast, free-living chimpanzees are renowned for their clever adaptations of twigs and leaves to serve as tools for obtaining both food and water.

Possibly gorillas have never been observed improvising tools to obtain food because the resources of their habitat meet their needs. Once, following a four-month dry spell in 1969, swarms of termites passed through the study area. I expected that the gorillas would, chimpanzee style, improvise twigs to extract the termites from the decayed tree stumps. However, they totally ignored the termites and waded their way past the infested areas to feed on surrounding vegetation.

On warm sunny days when group contentment is at its highest, feeding and resting periods are frequently accompanied by soft purring sounds resembling stomach rumbling; thus I named them "belch vocalizations." Typically, one animal expresses its feeling of well-being by giving a series of disyllabic belch vocalizations, naoom, naoom, naoom. This brings a chain of similar responses from other animals nearby, thus establishing both the location and the identification of the individuals participating in the exchange. The sound serves as the perfect communication for humans to imitate when initiating contacts with gorilla groups either partially or totally obscured in vegetation. By its use I can inform the animals of my presence and

allay any apprehensions they might have on hearing the noise of vegetation being broken near them. It is an extraordinary feeling to be able to sit in the middle of a resting group of gorillas and contribute to a contented chorus of belch vocalizers. The belch vocalization is the most common form of intragroup communication. In its prolonged form it expresses contentment, though a slightly shortened version may serve as a mild disciplinary rebuke toward young animals. A stronger disciplinary vocalization is the "pig-grunt," a series of harsh, staccato grunts resembling the sounds of pigs feeding at a sty, and frequently used by silverbacks when settling squabbles among other members of their groups. Females direct the vocalization toward other adults when conflicts over food arise or when right-of-way on trails occurs, and also toward their infants, particularly during the last stages of the weaning process. Young individuals will pig-grunt among themselves when complaining during rough play with their siblings or peers.

Popular literature generally describes roars, screams, or wraaghs as the main components of the gorilla vocabulary. Indeed, during the initial part of my study, these were the most frequent sounds I heard from the as yet unhabituated gorillas whenever my presence posed an element of threat to them. Gorilla vocalizations have always interested me, and I have spent many months recording sounds in the field and later analyzing them spectrographically at Cambridge University. The work proved most rewarding when the high frequency of alarm calls was slowly replaced by undisturbed intragroup vocalizations, sounds I used to gain further acceptance by the gorillas.

In late 1972, when student observers began working at Karisoke, instruction in the art of belch vocalizing was one of the first lessons taught. Several newcomers never quite got on to imitating the sound properly. One person's rendition of the belch vocalization sounded exactly like a goat's bleat, but within several weeks, the gorillas even became accustomed to his individual greeting call.

At times, students as well as I have unexpectedly encountered gorillas before we were aware of the animals' nearness. Such occasions could provoke charges, especially if interactions were occurring between groups, when the animals were traveling in a precarious range area (like one frequented by poachers), or if an infant had recently been born.

Understandably, such circumstances compelled highly protective strategies from a group's silverback leader. Once I was charged when climbing through tall vegetation up a steep hill to meet Group 8, thought to be several hours away. Suddenly, like a pane of broken glass, the air around me was shattered by the screams of the five males of the group as they bulldozed their way down through the foliage toward me. It is very difficult to describe the charge of a gorilla group. As in the other charges I have experienced, the intensity of the gorillas' screams was so deafening, I could not locate the source of the noise. I only knew that the group was charging from above, when the tall vegetation gave way as though an out-of-control tractor were headed directly for me.

Upon recognizing me, the group's dominant silverback swiftly braked to a stop three feet away, causing the four males behind him, momentarily and ungracefully, to pile up on top of him. At this instant I slowly sank to the ground to assume as submissive a pose as possible. The hair on each male's headcrest stood erect (piloerection), canines were fully exposed, the irises of ordinarily soft brown eyes glinted yellow — more like those of cats than of gorillas — and an overpowering fear odor permeated the air. For a good half-hour all five males screamed if I made even the slightest movement. After a thirty-minute period, the group allowed me to pretend to feed meekly on vegetation before they finally moved rigidly out of sight uphill.

Only then could I stand up to check out the cause of human shouting that I had heard coming from the base of the slope about four hundred feet below. There, standing along a trail used extensively for cattle at this early stage of my work, stood a group of Watutsi herdsmen. They had been drawn by the gorillas' screams from various parts of the adjacent forest where they were grazing cattle. I later learned the men were certain I had been torn to shreds, and upon seeing me stand upright were convinced that I was protected by a very special kind of *sumu* against the wrath of the gorillas, whom they feared deeply.

Once the men moved out of sight I continued to follow Group 8 — at a distance — to discover that they had been interacting with Group 9 when I had attempted to contact them. Trail sign indicated Group 9 had also taken part in the charge but had halted before reaching me. It was only when descending the slope that I discovered a lone silverback directly below me. His presence made Group 8's charge far more understandable. Upon hearing the sounds of my approach through the thick vegetation, the gorillas probably thought I was the lone male whose presence neither group would have tolerated.

Though you know the charging gorillas are simply acting defensively and do not wish to inflict physical harm, you instinctively want to flee, an impulse that automatically invites a chase. I have always been convinced of the intrinsically gentle nature of gorillas and felt their charges were basically bluff in nature, so never hesitated to hold my ground. However, because of the intensity of their screams and the speed of their approaches, I found it possible to face charging gorillas only by clinging to surrounding vegetation for dear life. Without that support, I surely would have turned tail and run.

Like all charges, this one was really my fault for having climbed the steep slope to approach directly beneath the animals without first identifying myself. Other charges have occurred when students, also accidentally, made the same error. Some census workers who encountered unfamiliar gorilla groups outside the study area had to return to their camps several times to change clothes because of reflexive reactions prompted by charges. People who hold their ground usually are not hurt unless they are unknown to the gorillas, But even then they only occasionally receive a moderate slap from a passing animal. People who run are not so fortunate.

A very capable student once made the same mistake as I had when approaching Group 8 from directly below. He was climbing through extremely dense foliage in a poacher area and noisily hacking at vegetation with his *panga*, not knowing the group was near. The faulty approach provoked a charge from the dominant silverback, who could not see who was coming. When the young man instinctively turned and ran, the male lunged toward the fleeing form. The gorilla knocked him down, tore into his knapsack, and was just beginning to sink his teeth into the student's arm when he recognized a familiar observer. The silverback immediately backed off, wearing what I was told was an "apologetic facial expression" before scurrying back to the rest of Group 8 without even a backward glance.

Another person who ran away from the charge of an unfamiliar group was someone who had always scoffed at the idea of pacifying gorillas with introductory vocalizations on approaching them. His actions around gorillas were often jerky and almost aggressive in nature He was able to spend nearly a year working with habituated animals before his luck ran out. In the lead of a large boisterous group of tourists he approached two interacting groups from directly below and was instantly charged by a silverback, who rolled with him for some thirty feet, breaking three of his ribs, and then bit deeply into the dorsal surface of the man's neck. The bite would have been fatal had it pierced the jugular vein on the neck's ventral surface. This person survived to brag about his "close shave" without acknowledging his violation of basic gorilla protocol.

In another incident a young tourist tried to pick up an infant from Group 5 "to cuddle" in spite of the alarmed screams given by the group. Before he got his hands on the youngster, the infant's mother and the group's silverback defensively charged, causing the boy to turn and run. He fell and both gorilla parents were instantly on his back, biting him and tearing at his clothing. Many months later in Ruhengeri I saw that he still bore deep scars from the encounter on his legs and arms.

Charge anecdotes do the gorilla an injustice. Were it not for human encroachment into their terrain, the animals undoubtedly would have to charge only when defending their familial groups from intrusion by other gorillas. I remain deeply concerned about having habituated gorillas to human beings. This is one reason I do not habituate them to members of my African staff. Gorillas have known Africans only as poachers in the past. The second that it takes a gorilla to determine if an African is friend or foe is the second that might cost the animal its life from a spear, arrow, or bullet.

How ironic it is that probably less than a hundred men, armed with bows and arrows, spears or guns, have been allowed to plague the wildlife in the parklands that form the last stronghold for the mountain gorilla. The strongest counterstrategy against the abuse encroachers bestow upon the wildlife of the Virungas may be that of active conservation. Active conservation is a straightforward issue. It begins with providing personal incentive on a one-to-one basis with individual Africans, not only to take pride in their park but also to assume personally some of the responsibility toward the protection of their heritage. Given the incentive, active conservation is accomplished by very fundamental needs such as boots for the rangers' feet, decent clothing and raingear, ample food, and adequate wages. Thus equipped, hundreds of antipoacher patrols have set out from Karisoke into the heartland of the Virungas to cut traps, confiscate encroachers' weapons, and release newly trapped animals from snares. Active conservation within a steadily shrinking internationally designated sanctuary filled with poachers, traps, herdsmen, farmers, and beekeepers needs to be supplemented by Rwandese and Zairoise enforcement of anti-encroacher laws as well as severe penalties for the illegal sale of poached animals for their meat, skins, tusks, or for financial profits. Active conservation does not rule out any other long-term conservation approaches.

Theoretical conservation as a sole conservation effort is in marked contrast to active conservation. To an impoverished country such as Rwanda, an abstract rather than practical approach is more appealing. Theoretical conservation seeks to encourage growth in tourism by improving existing roads that circle the mountains of the Parc des Volcans, by renovating the park headquarters and tourists lodging and by the habituation of gorillas near the park boundaries for tourists to visit and photograph. Theoretical conservation is lauded highly by Rwandese government and park officials, who are understandably eager to see the Parc des Volcans gain international acclaim and to justify its economic existence in a land-scarce country, these efforts attract increasing numbers of sightseers to the

Parc des Volcans. In 1980 alone, the park's revenue from tourism more than doubled over that received in 1979.

There is a failure to realize that the immediate needs of some 200 remaining mountain gorilla, and also of other Virunga wildlife now struggling for survival on a day-to-day basis, are not met by the long-term goals of theoretical conservation. Gorillas and the other park animals do not have time to wait. It takes only one trap, one bullet to kill a gorilla. For this reason it is mandatory that conservation efforts be actively concentrated on the immediate perils existing within the park. Next to these efforts, all others become theoretical. Educating the local populace to respect gorillas and working to attract tourism do not help the 242 remaining gorillas of the Virungas survive for future generations of tourists to enjoy. Theoretical conservation has good long-term goals that needlessly ignore desperate immediate needs.

Far from the public's eye active conservation continues in the Parc des Volcans with a handful of dedicated people who work tirelessly behind the scenes to protect the park and its wildlife. One outstanding person who risked his position for what he believed, is Paulin Nkubili. As Rwandese Chef des Brigades, he inflicted strong penalties upon both buyers' and sellers' game illegally poached from the Parc des Volcans. By his actions, he also essentially eliminated the trophy market involving the sale of gorillas' heads and hands for souvenirs. There are some members of the Watutsi clan of Rutshema, a people who for generations grazed cattle illegally in the park, who themselves became active

conservationists by leading antipoacher patrols in the Virungas. Paulin Nkubili, loyal members of the Karisoke Research Centre staff, and those of the patrols are each personally motivated in their unheralded efforts and rewarded only in the knowledge of their accomplishments. The hope for the future of the Virungas lies in the hands of just such individuals.

Chapter 7

Flo and Her Family

Jane Goodall

OLD FLO LAY ON HER BACK in the early morning sunshine her belly full of palm nuts, and suspended Flint above her, grasping one of his minute wrists with her large horny foot. As he dangled, gently saving his free arm and kicking with his legs, she reached up and tickled him in his groin and his neck until he opened his mouth in the place-face, or chimpanzee smile. Nearby Fifi sat staring at Flint, occasionally reaching out to touch her ten-week-old brother gently with one hand.

Faben and Figan, Flo's two elder sons, played with each other not far away. Since Flint's birth two and a half months earlier Faben had begun to move around with his family more frequently. Every so often, as their game became extra vigorous, I could hear the panting chuckles of chimpanzee laughter. All at once Faben, three or four years Figan's senior, began to play rather roughly, sitting down and kicking with the soles of his feet on Figan's bent head. After a few moments Figan had had enough. He left Faben, and, with his jaunty walk, approached Fifi and tried to play with her. At that moment Flo, gathering Flint to her breast, got up to move into the shade, and Fifi pulled away from Figan to follow her mother. Ever since Hugo and I had returned to the Gombe Stream when Flint was seven weeks old, Fifi had become increasingly fascinated by her new brother.

Flo sat down and began to tickle Fint's neck with small nibbling movements of her worn teeth, and Fifi once again sat close and reached out to make a few grooming movements on Flint's back. Flo ignored this. Earlier, though, when Flint was not yet two months old, Flo had usually pushed Fifi's hand away each time she tried to touch Flint, and often the only way in which the child had been able to momentarily touch the infant had been by solicitously grooming Flo, working ever closer and closer to those places where Flint's hands gripped his mother's hair. Intently Fifi had groomed around the hands, occasionally briefly fondling the minute fingers and then, with a glance at Flo, hastily returning to her grooming.

Now, however, Flint was older and for the most part Fifi was permitted to touch him. As I watched, Fifi began to play with Flint, taking one hand and nibbling the fingers. Flint gave a soft whimper — possibly Fifi had hurt him — and instantly Flo pushed her daughter's hand away and cuddled her infant close. Frustrated, Fifi rocked slightly to and fro, twisting her arms behind her head and staring at Flint, her lips slightly pouted. It was not long before she reached out, gently this time, to touch him again.

I have always thought that human children become increasingly fascinating as they grow out of the helpless baby stage and begin to respond to people and things. Certainly a chimpanzee baby becomes more attractive as it grows older, not only to its mother and siblings but also to the other members of the community — and to mere human observers. For Hugo and me the privilege of being able to watch Flint's progress that year remains one of the most delightful of our experiences — comparable only to the joy we were to know much later as we watched our own son growing up.

When Flint was three months old he was able to pull himself about on Flo's body, taking handfuls of her hair, pulling with his arms and pushing with his feet. And at this time he began to respond when Fifi approached by reaching out toward her. Fifi became more and more preoccupied with him. She began to make repeated attempts to pull him away from his mother. At first Flo firmly prevented this, but even when Fifi persisted, continually pulling at her brother, Flo never punished her. Sometimes she pushed the child's hand away, sometimes she simply walked away, leaving Fifi rocking slightly, her limbs contorted. And sometimes, when Fifi was extra troublesome, Flo instead of repulsing her advances either groomed her or played with her quite vigorously. These activities usually served to distract Fifi's attention, at least temporarily, from her infant brother.

As the year wore on it seemed that Flow, perhaps as a result of playing so often with her two younger children, became even more playful. Often, as the weeks passed, we saw her playing with both Figan and twelve-year-old Faben, tickling them or chasing with them round and round a tree trunk with Flint hanging on for dear life. On one occasion, in the middle of a romp with Faben, this old female lowered her balding head to the ground, raised her bony rump in the air, and actually turned a somersault. And then, almost as though she felt slightly ridiculous, she moved away, sat down, and began to groom Flint very carefully.

When Flint was thirteen weeks old we saw Fifi succeed in pulling him away from his mother. Flo was grooming Figan when Fifi, with infinite caution and many quick glances toward her mother's face, began to pull at Flint's foot. Inch by inch she drew the infant toward her — and all at once he was in her arms. Fifi lay on her back and cuddled Flint to her tummy with her arms and legs. She lay very still.

To our surprise Flo for the first few moments appeared to take no notice at all. But when Flint, who had possibly never lost contact with his mother's body, reached around and held his arms toward her, pouting his lips and uttering a soft *hoo* of distress, Flo instantly gathered him to her breast and bent to kiss his head with her lips. Flint eagerly sought the reassurance of his mother's breast, suckling for a few moments before turning to look at Fifi again. And Fifi, her hands clasped behind her head, her elbows in the air, stared at Flint. Ten minutes later Fifi was again permitted to hold Flint for a short while but, once more, the moment Flint gave his tiny distressed whimper Flo rescued him; and Flint, as before, suckled briefly when he regained the security of his mother's arms.

After this not a day passed without Fifi pulling her infant brother away from Flo. As time went on Flint became accustomed to the arms of his sibling, and she was able to hold him for longer periods before he uttered the tiny sound that for the next nine months would bring Flo hastening to his rescue. Flo even permitted Fifi to carry Flint when the family wandered through the forests.

On those occasions when Flo and her family were part of a large group, however, Flo was more possessive of her infant. Then if Fifi moved away with Flint, Flo followed, uttering soft whimpers herself, until she caught up with the kidnaper and retrieved her infant. Even now Fifi was not punished; Flo simply reached forward, grabbed hold of her daughter's ankle, and then gathered Flint into her arms. Sometimes Fifi led her old mother a merry dance, around trees, under low vegetation, where Flo had to creep almost on her belly — even up into the trees. And sometimes, as if to prevent Flo from catching hold of her, she walked backward in front of her mother, grunting softly and bobbing up and down as though in submission, but not — until she was forced to — relinquishing Flint.

When Flint was very small his two elder brothers, although they sometimes stared at him, paid him little attention. Occasionally while he was grooming with his mother, Faben very gently patted the infant; Figan, though he was such an integral part of the family, seemed afraid to touch Flint in the early days. If, when Figan and Flo were grooming, the infant accidentally touched Figan, as in baby fashion he waved his arms about, Figan, after a quick glance at Flo's face, seemed to avoid looking at Flint. For Figan, though he was a vigorous adolescent male, still showed great respect for his old mother.

One occasion is vivid in my memory. Fifi had taken Flint and was sitting grooming the infant some ten yards from Flo. When Figan approached and sat beside his sister, Flint turned toward him and, with his wide-eyed gaze fixed on Figan's face, reached out to grasp his brother's chest hair. Figan started, and after a quick glance in Flo's direction raised his hands up and away from the infant. Then he stayed motionless, staring down at Flint, his lips tense. The infant pulled closer and nuzzled at Figan's breast, then all at once seemed afraid of the unfamiliar. Usually his only contacts were Flo and Fifi, and if he reached toward either of them they always responded by holding him close. With a slight pout Flint turned back to Fifi, but then, as though confused, he again reached to Figan with a soft whimper. At this Flo came hurrying to his rescue, and as she approached Figan too gave low worried cries, and raised his hands even higher as in the age-old gesture of surrender. Flow gathered up her infant and Figan lowered his hands slowly, as though dazed.

One day, when Flint was just less than five months old, Flo got up to go and, instead of pressing Flint to her belly, took his arm in one hand and hoisted him over her shoulder onto her back. There he remained for a few yards before he slipped down and clung to her arm. For a short distance Flo continued, with Flint gripping around her elbow; then she pushed him back under her tummy. The next day when Flo arrived in camp, Flint was clinging precariously to her back, hanging on to her sparse hair with his hands and feet. When Flo left she again pushed her son up onto her back, and again he clung there awhile before sliding down and dangling from one hand by her side. This time, after walking thirty yards or so, Flo pushed him once more onto her back. After this Flint nearly always rode on Flo's back or else dangled beside her while she walked the mountains. This was not surprising, since all infants after a certain age start riding their mothers rather than clinging on beneath; but we were astonished to see that Fifi, when next we saw her take Flint, also tried to push him onto her back. This was surely an example of learning by direct observation of her mother's behavior.

By the time Flint was five months old he had become an accomplished rider, and only occasionally slipped down to dangle beside Flow as she walked. If there was any sign of excitement among the group, or if Flo was about to move into thick undergrowth, then she always reached back and pushed Flint around so that he clung underneath as before. Soon he learned to wriggle under Flo of his own accord in response to the slightest touch.

About the same time Flint began to ride on Flo's back we first saw him take a step by himself. For some weeks previously he had been able to stand on the ground balanced on three limbs and clinging to Flo's hair with one hand; and occasionally he had taken a couple of steps in this manner. On this particular morning he suddenly let go of Flo and stood by himself, all four limbs on the ground. Then, very deliberately, he lifted one hand off the ground, moved it

forward safely, and paused. He lifted a foot off the ground, lurched sideways, staggered, and fell on his nose with a whimper. Instantly Flo reached out and scooped him into her arms. But that was the beginning. Each day after this Flint walked one or two steps farther, although for months he was incredibly wobbly. Constantly he got his hands and feet muddled up and fell — and always Flo was quick to gather him up. Often she kept one hand under his tummy as he tottered along.

Just after he began to walk Flint attempted to climb. One day we saw him standing upright, holding on to a tiny sapling with both hands and gripping it first with one foot and then the other. But he never managed to get both feet off the ground at once and after a few moments he fell backward onto the ground. Subsequently he repeated this performance several times and Flo, as she groomed Fifi, idly held one hand behind his back, preventing further tumbles. A week after his first attempt Flint was able to climb a short way quite easily. Like a human child, he found it much harder to get down by himself. Flo of course was very watchful — as indeed was Fifi — and one or other of his guardians reached to rescue him the moment he gave his soft whimper. Flo, in fact, often retrieved him when she noticed that the end of the branch on which he was swinging was beginning to bend and Flint was totally unaware of it. She was equally quick to seize him if she saw any sign of social excitement or aggression among other members of the group.

Gradually Flint learned to control his limbs slightly better when walking, although he still often relied on speed, rather than coordination, to get him from one place to another. He began to venture several yards away from Flo — and since any movement away from his mother was wildly exciting, and excitement set his hair on end, he tottered around like a fluffy black ball, his wide-eyed gaze fixed with concentration on some object or individual in front of him.

It was at this time that fascination for her small brother became almost an obsession of Fifi's. She spent nearly all her day laying with him, grooming him as he slept, or carrying him about with her. Flo, it seemed, was often far from displeased to shed from time to time part of her load of maternal responsibility. Provided that Fifi did not carry Flint out of sight, and provided there were no potentially aggressive males nearby, she no longer objected when Fifi kidnapped Flint. Nor did Flo seem to mind if other youngsters approached Flint to play gently with him. But Fifi did. If she suddenly noticed Gilka, or another of her erstwhile playmates, close to Flint, Fifi instantly abandoned whatever she was doing, rushed over and chased the youngster away, hair bristling, arms flailing, and feet stamping the ground. Even chimps much older than herself, provided they were subordinate to Flo, were threatened or even attacked by aggressive Fifi. Presumably she acted on the assumption that if anything went wrong old Flo would hurry to her assistance — and it was more evident that the victims of her fury were fully aware of this fact also.

Fifi, however, could not chase Faben or Figan away from Flint, and as the infant grew up both of this elder brothers showed the increasing interest in him.

Often they would approach and play with him, tickling him or pushing him gently to and fro as he dangled, legs kicking, from a low branch. Sometimes when Figan was playing with Flint, we saw Fifi hurry to the scene and try to initiate a game with Figan; many times she was successful. Then, when the game was over, Fifi would hurry back to play with Flint herself. Was she, perhaps, practicing the same technique of distraction that Flo had used so often on her?

When Flint tottered up to one of the adult males, Fifi could scarcely interfere; she merely sat and stared as David, or Goliath, or Mike reached out and time and again patted Flint or gently embraced him. And as the weeks went by Flint, like a spoiled human child, wanted more and more attention. One day as he tottered up to Mr. McGregor the old male got up and moved away. It was not, I think, deliberate — it just happened that he was about to leave. Flint stopped dead, staring with widening eyes at the male's retreating rear, and then, stumbling along with frantic haste, repeatedly falling on his face, Flint followed. Continuously he uttered his soft whimper. Within moments Flo was rushing to retrieve him. That was only the start of it, and for the next few weeks Flint was always whimpering along after one or other of the adult makes who had not deigned to stop and greet him, or who had walked away from the infant for any reason whatever. Often the male concerned, uneasy perhaps at the little calls following in his wake, would stop or turn back to pat Flint.

When Flint was eight months old he sometimes spent fifteen minutes or so out of contact with Flo as he played or explored, but he was never far from her. He was somewhat steadier on his feet and he was able to join Fifi in some of her slightly rougher games, chasing around a grass tuft, or pulling himself on top of her as she lay on the ground and tickling her with his hands and mouth. It was at this time that the termiting season began.

One day when Flo was fishing for termites it became obvious that Figan and Fifi, who had been eating termites at the same heap, were becoming restless and wanted to leave. Old Flo, who had already fished for two hours and was herself only getting about two termites every five minutes, showed no signs of stopping. Being an old female, it was possible that she might continue for another hour at least. Several times Figan had set off resolutely along the track leading to the stream, but on each occasion, after repeatedly looking back at Flow, he had given up and returned to wait for his mother.

Flint, too young to mind where he was, pottered about on the heap, occasionally dabbing at a termite. Suddenly Figan got up and again this time approached Flint. Adopting the posture of a mother who signals her infant to climb onto her back, Figan bent one leg and reached back his hand to Flint, uttering a soft, pleading wimper. Flint tottered up to him at once, and Figan, still whimpering, put his hand under Flint and gently pushed him onto his back. Once Flint was safely aboard, Figan, with another quick glance at Flow, set off rapidly along the track. A moment later Flo discarded her tool and followed.

Hugo and I were amazed at this further example of Figan's ingenuity in getting his own way. Had his behavior really been deliberate? We couldn't be sure. A few days later Fifi did exactly the same thing. A week later we watched Faben take Flint to his breast after he too had tried several times to persuade his mother to follow him away from a termite heap. We had never seen Faben carrying Flint before.

As the termite season wore on there could be no doubt that Flo's older offspring were kidnaping Flint with the deliberate intent of getting their mother to stop, at least for the time being, her endless termiting. We saw all three of them taking Flint in this way on any number of occasions. They were not always successful. Often Flint dropped off and ran back to his mother of his own accord. And sometimes, if Flo's hole was still yielding a good supply of termites, she hurried to retrieve Flint and then returned to the heap followed by the unsuccessful kidnaper — who usually tried again later.

Flint, of course, was too young to show any interest in eating termites; he occasionally sampled a mouthful of fig or banana but still received virtually all his nourishment from his mother's milk, and would continue to do so for another year. Once in a while he did poke at a crawling termite with his finger, and he played with discarded grass tools when he was wandering about on a termite heap. Also, he began to "mop" everything. When termites are spilled onto the surface of the heap, older chimps mop them up with the backs of their wrists: the termites become entangled in the hairs and are picked off with the lips. It was soon after the termite season began that Flint started to mop things — the ground, his own legs, his mother's back as he rode along, anything but termites. Actually, though he sometimes gazed intently for a few moments as his mother or one of his siblings worked, he was not really interested in this activity which so absorbed his elders.

Fifi, on the other hand, was a keen termite fisher, and when Flint, wanting to play with his sister, jumped onto her and scattered the insects from her grass stem, she was obviously irritated. Over and over she pushed him away roughly. Fifi still played with Flint frequently herself when she was not termiting, but, almost as though some spell had been broken, she never again showed quite the same fanatical preoccupation with him; she no longer protected him as consistently from social contact with other young chimps.

Flint then began to enlarge his circle of friends, since Fifi, particularly when she was working at a termite heap, often permitted Gilka or one of the other juveniles to approach and play with Flint. She no longer rushed up aggressively every time one or other of the adolescent females carried Flint around or groomed him or played with him. Flint, in fact, was growing up.

Even when Fifi did devote all her attention to her little brother she could no longer treat him as her doll, for he had developed a mind of his own. If Fifi wanted to carry him in one direction and he wanted to go somewhere else, then he struggled away from her and went his way. Also, he was getting heavier. One day when Flint was sleeping in her lap and gripping tightly to her hair, it was obvious that he was hurting his sister. Fifi carefully detached first one hand and then the other, but as soon as they were loosened Flint, disturbed, gripped on again tightly. Finally, for the first time on record Fifi carried the infant back to Flo and pushed him in her mother's direction.

When Flint was one year old he was still wobbly on his legs but he was quick to bounce toward any game in progress, and eager to hurry over to greet any newcomer that joined his group. He was, in fact, beginning to take part in the social life of his community: a community which at that time was still unsettled as a result of the dramatic rise to overall dominance of Mike. Flint could scarcely have been aware of the battle of wills that had finally led to Goliath's defeat because it had started at the time of his birth. Flint grew up in a world where Mike undisputedly was supreme.

Chapter 8

Are We in Anthropodenial?

By Frans de Waal

Wʜᴇɴ ɢᴜᴇsᴛs ᴀʀʀɪᴠᴇ ᴀᴛ ᴛʜᴇ Yerkes Regional Primate Research Center in Georgia, where I work, they usually pay a visit to the chimpanzees. And often, when she sees them approaching the compound, an adult female chimpanzee named Georgia will hurry to the spigot to collect a mouthful of water. She'll then casually mingle with the rest of the colony behind the mesh fence, and not even the sharpest observer will notice anything unusual. If necessary, Georgia will wait minutes, with her lips closed, until the visitors come near. Then there will be shrieks, laughs, jumps—and sometimes falls—when she suddenly sprays them.

I have known quite a few apes that are good at surprising people, naive and otherwise. Heini Hediger, the great Swiss zoo biologist, recounts how he—being prepared to meet the challenge and paying attention to the ape's every move—got drenched by an experienced chimpanzee. I once found myself in a similar situation with Georgia; she had taken a drink from the spigot and was sneaking up to me. I looked her straight in the eye and pointed my finger at her, warning in Dutch, "I have seen you!" She immediately stepped back, let some of the water dribble from her mouth, and swallowed the rest. I certainly do not wish to claim that she understands Dutch, but she must have sensed that I knew what she was up to, and that I was not going to be an easy target.

To endow animals with human emotions has long been a scientific taboo. But if we do not, we risk missing something fundamental, about both animals and us.

Now, no doubt even a casual reader will have noticed that in describing Georgia's actions, I've implied human qualities such as intentions, the ability to interpret my own awareness, and a tendency toward mischief. Yet scientific tradition says I should avoid such language—I am committing the sin of anthropomorphism, of turning nonhumans into humans. The word comes from the Greek, meaning "human form," and it was the ancient Greeks who first gave the practice a bad reputation. They did not have chimpanzees in mind: the philosopher Xenophanes objected to Homer's poetry because it treated Zeus and the other gods as if they were people. How could we be so arrogant, Xenophanes asked, as to think that the gods should look like us? If horses could draw pictures, he suggested mockingly, they would no doubt make their gods look like horses.

Nowadays the intellectual descendants of Xenophanes warn against perceiving animals to be like ourselves. There are, for example, the behaviorists, who follow psychologist B. F. Skinner in viewing the actions of animals as responses shaped by rewards and punishments rather than the result of internal decision making, emotions, or intentions. They would say that Georgia was not "up to" anything when she sprayed water on her victims. Far from planning and executing a naughty plot, Georgia merely fell for the irresistible reward of human surprise and annoyance. Whereas any person acting like her would be scolded, arrested, or held accountable, Georgia is somehow innocent.

Behaviorists are not the only scientists who have avoided thinking about the inner life of animals. Some sociobiologists—researchers who look for the roots of behavior in evolution—depict animals as "survival machines" and "pre-programmed robots" put on Earth to serve their "selfish" genes. There is a certain metaphorical value to these concepts, but is has been negated by the misunderstanding they've created. Such language can give the impression that only genes are entitled to an inner life. No more delusively anthropomorphizing idea has been put forward since the pet-rock craze of the 1970s. In fact, during evolution, genes—a mere batch of molecules—simply multiply at different rates, depending on the traits they produce in an individual. To say that genes are selfish is like saying a snowball growing in size as it rolls down a hill is greedy for snow.

Logically, these agnostic attitudes toward a mental life in animals can be valid only if they're applied to our own species as well. Yet it's uncommon to find researchers who try to study human behavior as purely a matter of reward and punishment. Describe a person as having intentions, feelings, and thoughts and you most likely won't encounter much resistance. Our own familiarity with our inner lives overrules whatever some school of thought might claim about us. Yet despite this double standard toward behavior in humans and animals, modern biology leaves us no choice other than to conclude that we *are* animals. In terms of anatomy, physiology, and neurology we are really no more exceptional than, say, an elephant or a platypus is in its own way. Even such presumed hallmarks of humanity as warfare, politics, culture, morality, and language may not be completely unprecedented. For example, different groups of wild chimpanzees employ different technologies—some fish for termites with sticks, others crack nuts with stones—that are transmitted from one generation to the next through a process reminiscent of human culture.

Given these discoveries, we must be very careful not to exaggerate the uniqueness of our species. The ancients apparently never gave much thought to this practice, the opposite of anthropomorphism, and so we lack a word for it. I will call it anthropodenial: a blindness to the human-like characteristics of other animals, or the animal-like characteristics of ourselves.

Those who are in anthropodenial try to build a brick wall to separate humans from the rest of the animal kingdom. They carry on the tradition of René Descartes, who declared that while humans possessed souls, animals were mere automatons. This produced a serious dilemma when Charles Darwin came along: If we descended from such automatons, were we not automatons ourselves? If not, how did we get to be so different?

Each time we must ask such a question, another brick is pulled out of the dividing wall, and to me this wall is beginning to look like a slice of Swiss cheese. I work on a daily basis with animals from which it is about as hard to distance yourself as from "Lucy," the famed 3.2-million-year-old fossil australopithecine. If we owe Lucy the respect of an ancestor, does this not force a different look at the apes? After all, as far as we can tell, the most significant difference between Lucy and modern chimpanzees is found in their hips, not their craniums.

As soon as we admit that animals are far more like our relatives than like machines, then anthropodenial becomes impossible and anthropomorphism becomes inevitable—and scientifically acceptable. But not *all* forms of anthropomorphism, of course. Popular culture bombards us with examples of animals being humanized for all sorts of purposes, ranging from education to entertainment to satire to propaganda. Walt Disney, for example, made us forget that Mickey is a mouse, and Donald a duck. George Orwell laid a cover of human societal ills over a population of livestock. I was once struck by an advertisement for an oil company that claimed its propane saved the environment, in which a grizzly bear enjoying a pristine landscape had his arm around his mate's shoulders. In fact, bears are nearsighted and do not form pair-bonds, so the image says more about our own behavior than theirs.

Perhaps that was the intent. The problem is, we do not always remember that, when used in this way, anthropomorphism can provide insight only into human affairs and not into the affairs of animals. When my book *Chimpanzee Politics* came out in France, in 1987, my publisher decided (unbeknownst to me) to put François Mitterrand and Jacques Chirac on the cover with a chimpanzee between them. I can only assume he wanted to imply that these politicians acted like "mere" apes. Yet by doing so he went completely against the whole point of my book, which was not to ridicule people but to show that chimpanzees live in complex societies full of alliances and power plays that in some ways mirror our own.

You can often hear similar attempts at anthropomorphic humor in the crowds that form around the monkey exhibit at a typical zoo. Isn't it interesting that antelopes, lions, and giraffes rarely elicit hilarity? But people who watch primates end up hooting and yelling, scratching themselves in exaggeration, and pointing at the animals while shouting, "I had to look twice, Larry. I thought it was you!" In my mind, the laughter reflects anthropodenial: it is a nervous reaction caused by an uncomfortable resemblance.

That very resemblance, however, can allow us to make better use of anthropomorphism, but for this we must view it as a means rather than an end. It should not be our goal to find some quality in an animal that is precisely equivalent to an aspect of our own inner lives. Rather, we should use the fact that we are similar to animals to develop ideas we can test. For example, after observing a group of chimpanzees at length, we begin to suspect that some individuals are attempting to "deceive" others—by giving false alarms to distract unwanted attention from the theft of food or from forbidden sexual activity. Once we frame the observation in such terms, we can devise testable predictions. We can figure out just what it would take to demonstrate deception on the part of chimpanzees. In this way, a speculation is turned into a challenge.

Naturally, we must always be on guard. To avoid making silly interpretations based on anthropomorphism, one must always interpret animal behavior in the wider context of a species' habits and natural history. Without experience with primates, one could imagine that a grinning rhesus monkey must be delighted, or that a chimpanzee running toward another with loud grunts must be in an aggressive mood. But primatologists know from many hours of observation that rhesus monkeys bare their teeth when intimidated, and that chimpanzees often grunt when they meet and embrace. In other words, a grinning rhesus monkey signals submission, and a chimpanzee's grunting often serves as a greeting. A careful observer may thus arrive at an informed anthropomorphism that is at odds with extrapolations from human behavior.

One must also always be aware that some animals are more like ourselves than others. The problem of sharing the experiences of organisms that rely on different senses is a profound one. It was expressed most famously by the philosopher Thomas Nagel when he asked, "What is it like to be a bat?" A bat perceives its world in pulses of reflected sound, something we creatures of vision would have a hard time imagining. Perhaps even more alien would be the experience of an animal such as the star-nosed mole. With 22 pink, writhing tentacles around its nostrils, it is able to feel microscopic textures on small objects in the mud with the keenest sense of touch of any animal on Earth.

Humans can barely imagine a star-nosed mole's *Umwelt*—a German term for the environment as perceived by the animal. Obviously, the closer a species is to us, the easier it is to enter its *Umwelt*. This is why anthropomorphism is not only tempting in the case of apes but also hard to reject on the grounds that we cannot know how they perceive the world. Their sensory systems are essentially the same as ours.

LAST SUMMER, AN APE SAVED A three-year-old boy. The child, who had fallen 20 feet into the primate exhibit at Chicago's Brookfield Zoo, was scooped up and carried to safety by Binti Jua, an eight-year-old western lowland female gorilla. The gorilla sat down on a log in a stream, cradling the boy in her lap and patting his back, and then carried him to one of the exhibit doorways before laying him down and continuing on her way.

Binti became a celebrity overnight, figuring in the speeches of leading politicians who held her up as an example of much-needed compassion. Some scientists were less lyrical, however. They cautioned that Binti's motives might have been less noble than they appeared, pointing out that this gorilla had been

raised by people and had been taught parental skills with a stuffed animal. The whole affair might have been one of a confused maternal instinct, they claimed.

Bonobos have been known to assist companions new to their quarters in zoos, taking them by the hand to guide them through the maze of corridors connecting parts of their building.

The intriguing thing about this flurry of alternative explanations was that nobody would think of raising similar doubts when a person saves a dog hit by a car. The rescuer might have grown up around a kennel, have been praised for being kind to animals, have a nurturing personality, yet we would still see his behavior as an act of caring. Whey then, in Binti's case, was her background held against her? I am not saying that I know what went through Binti's head, but I do know that no one had prepared her for this kind of emergency and that it is unlikely that, with her own 17-month-old infant on her back, she was "maternally confused." How in the world could such a highly intelligent animal mistake a blond boy in sneakers and a red T-shirt for a juvenile gorilla? Actually, the biggest surprise was how surprised most people were. Students of ape behavior did not feel that Binti had done anything unusual. Jörg Hess, a Swiss gorilla expert, put it most bluntly, "The incident can be sensational only for people who don't know a thing about gorillas."

Binti's action made a deep impression mainly because it benefited a member of our own species, but in my work on the evolution of morality and empathy, I have encountered numerous instances of animals caring for one another. For example, a chimpanzee consoles a victim after a violent attack, placing an arm around him and patting his back. And

bonobos (or pygmy chimpanzees) have been known to assist companions new to their quarters in zoos, taking them by the hand to guide them through the maze of corridors connecting parts of their building. These kinds of cases don't reach the newspapers but are consistent with Binti's assistance to the unfortunate boy and the idea that apes have a capacity for sympathy.

The traditional bulwark against this sort of cognitive interpretation is the principle of parsimony—that we must make as few assumptions as possible when trying to construct a scientific explanation, and that assuming an ape is capable of something like sympathy is too great a leap. But doesn't that same principle of parsimony argue against assuming a huge cognitive gap when the evolutionary distance between humans and apes is so small? If two closely related species act in the same manner, their underlying mental processes are probably the same, too. The incident at the Brookfield Zoo shows how hard it is to avoid anthropodenial and anthropomorphism at the same time: in trying to avoid thinking of Binti as a human being, we run straight into the realization that Binti's actions make little sense if we refuse to assume intentions and feelings.

In the end we must ask: What kind of risk we are willing to take—the risk of underestimating animal mental life or the risk of overestimating it? There is no simple answer. But from an evolutionary perspective, Binti's kindness, like Georgia's mischief, is most parsimoniously explained in the same way we explain our own behavior—as the result of a complex, and familiar, inner life.

FRANS DE WAAL is a professor of psychology at Emory University and research professor at the Yerkes Regional Primate Research Center in Atlanta. He is the author of several books, including Chimpanzee Politics *and* Good Natured: The Origins of Right and Wrong in Humans and Other Animals. *His latest book, in collaboration with acclaimed wildlife photographer Frans Lanting, is* Bonobo: The Forgotten Ape, *published by the University of California Press (1997).*

Chapter 9

A Natural History of Peace

Robert M. Sapolsky

The Naked Ape

The evolutionary biologist Theodosius Dobzhansky once said, "All species are unique, but humans are uniquest." Humans have long taken pride in their specialness. But the study of other primates is rendering the concept of such human exceptionalism increasingly suspect.

Some of the retrenchment has been relatively palatable, such as with the workings of our bodies. Thus we now know that a baboon heart can be transplanted into a human body and work for a few weeks, and human blood types are coded in Rh factors named after the rhesus monkeys that possess similar blood variability.

More discomfiting is the continuum that has been demonstrated in the realm of cognition. We now know, for example, that other species invent tools and use them with dexterity and local cultural variation. Other primates display "semanticity" (the use of symbols to refer to objects and actions) in their communication in ways that would impress any linguist. And experiments have shown other primates to possess a "theory of mind," that is, the ability to recognize that different individuals can have different thoughts and knowledge.

Our purported uniqueness has been challenged most, however, with regard to our social life. Like the occasional human hermit, there are a few primates that are typically asocial (such as the orangutan). Apart from those, however, it turns out that one cannot understand a primate in isolation from its social group. Across the 150 or so species of primates, the larger the average social group, the larger the cortex relative to the rest of the brain. The fanciest part of the primate brain, in other words, seems to have been sculpted by evolution to enable us to gossip and groom, cooperate and cheat, and obsess about who is mating with whom. Humans, in short, are yet another primate with an intense and rich social life -- a fact that raises the question of whether primatology can teach us something about a rather important part of human sociality, war and peace.

It used to be thought that humans were the only savagely violent primate. "We are the only species that kills its own," one might have heard intoned portentously at the end of nature films several decades ago. That view fell by the wayside in the 1960s as it became clear that some other primates kill their fellows aplenty. Males kill; females kill. Some kill one another's infants with cold-blooded stratagems worthy of Richard III. Some use their toolmaking skills to fashion bigger and better cudgels. Some other primates even engage in what can only be called warfare -- organized, proactive group violence directed at other populations.

As field studies of primates expanded, what became most striking was the variation in social practices across species. Yes, some primate species have lives filled with violence, frequent and varied. But life among others is filled with communitarianism, egalitarianism, and cooperative child rearing.

Patterns emerged. In less aggressive species, such as gibbons or marmosets, groups tend to live in lush rain forests where food is plentiful and life is easy. Females and males tend to be the same size, and the males lack secondary sexual markers such as long, sharp canines or garish coloring. Couples mate for life, and males help substantially with child care. In violent species, on the other hand, such as baboons and rhesus monkeys, the opposite conditions prevail.

The most disquieting fact about the violent species was the apparent inevitability of their behavior. Certain species seemed simply to be the way they were, fixed products of the interplay of evolution and ecology, and that was that. And although human males might not be inflexibly polygamous or come with bright red butts and six-inch canines designed for tooth-to-tooth combat, it was clear that our species had at least as much in common with the violent primates as with the gentle ones. "In their nature" thus became "in our nature." This was the humans-as-killer-apes theory popularized by the writer Robert Ardrey, according to which humans have as much chance of becoming intrinsically peaceful as they have of growing prehensile tails.

That view always had little more scientific rigor than a Planet of the Apes movie, but it took a great deal of field research to figure out just what should supplant it. After decades' more work, the picture has become quite interesting. Some primate species, it turns out, are indeed simply violent or peaceful, with their behavior driven by their social structures and ecological settings. More important, however, some primate species can make peace despite violent traits that seem built into their natures. The challenge now is to figure out under what conditions that can happen, and whether humans can manage the trick themselves.

Pax Bonobo

Primatology has long been dominated by studies of the chimpanzee, due in large part to the phenomenally influential research of Jane Goodall, whose findings from her decades of observations in the wild have been widely disseminated. National Geographic specials based on Goodall's work would always include the reminder that chimps are our closest relatives, a notion underlined by the fact that we share an astonishing

98 percent of our DNA with them. And Goodall and other chimp researchers have carefully documented an endless stream of murders, cannibalism, and organized group violence among their subjects. Humans' evolutionary fate thus seemed sealed, smeared by the excesses of these first cousins.

But all along there has been another chimp species, one traditionally ignored because of its small numbers; its habitat in remote, impenetrable rain forests; and the fact that its early chroniclers published in Japanese. These skinny little creatures were originally called "pygmy chimps" and were thought of as uninteresting, some sort of regressed subspecies of the real thing. Now known as bonobos, they are today recognized as a separate and distinct species that taxonomically and genetically is just as closely related to humans as the standard chimp. And boy, is this ever a different ape.

Male bonobos are not particularly aggressive and lack the massive musculature typical of species that engage in a lot of fighting (such as the standard chimp). Moreover, the bonobo social system is female dominated, food is often shared, and there are well-developed means for reconciling social tensions. And then there is the sex.

Bonobo sex is the prurient highlight of primatology conferences, and leads parents to shield their children's eyes when watching nature films. Bonobos have sex in every conceivable position and some seemingly inconceivable ones, in pairs and groups, between genders and within genders, to greet each other and to resolve conflicts, to work off steam after a predator scare, to celebrate finding food or to cajole its sharing, or just because. As the sound bite has it, chimps are from Mars and bonobos are from Venus.

All is not perfect in the bonobo commune, and they still have hierarchies and conflict (why else invent conflict resolution?). Nonetheless, they are currently among the trendiest of species to analyze, a wonderful antidote to their hard-boiled relatives. The trouble is, while we have a pretty good sense of what bonobos are like, we have little insight into how they got that way. Furthermore, this is basically what all bonobos seem to be like -- a classic case of in-their-nature-ness. There is even recent evidence for a genetic component to the phenomenon, in that bonobos (but not chimps) possess a version of a gene that makes affiliative behavior (behavior that promotes group cohesion) more pleasurable to males. So -- a wondrous species (and one, predictably, teetering on the edge of extinction). But besides being useful for taking the wind out of we-be-chimps fatalists, the bonobo has little to say to us. We are not bonobos, and never can be.

Warriors, Come Out To Play

In contrast to the social life of bonobos, the social life of chimps is not pretty. Nor is that of rhesus monkeys, nor savanna baboons -- a species found in groups of 50 to 100 in the African grasslands and one I have studied for close to 30 years. Hierarchies among baboons are strict, as are their consequences. Among males, high rank is typically achieved by a series of successful violent challenges. Spoils, such as meat, are unevenly divided. Most males die of the consequences of violence, and roughly half of their aggression is directed at third parties (some high-ranking male in a bad mood takes it out on an innocent bystander, such as a female or a subordinate male).

Male baboons, moreover, can fight amazingly dirty. I saw this happen a few years ago in one of the troops I study: Two males had fought, and one, having been badly trounced, assumed a crouching stance, with his rear end up in the air. This is universally recognized among savanna baboons as an abject gesture of subordination, signaling an end to the conflict, and the conventional response on the part of the victorious male is to subject the other to a ritualized gesture of dominance (such as mounting him). In this instance, however, the winner, approaching the loser as if to mount him, instead abruptly gave him a deep slash with his canines.

A baboon group, in short, is an unlikely breeding ground for pacifists. Nevertheless, there are some interesting exceptions. In recent years, for example, it has been recognized that a certain traditional style of chest-thumping evolutionary thinking is wrong. According to the standard logic, males compete with one another aggressively in order to achieve and maintain a high rank, which will in turn enable them to dominate reproduction and thus maximize the number of copies of their genes that are passed on to the next generation. But

although aggression among baboons does indeed have something to do with attaining a high rank, it turns out to have virtually nothing to do with maintaining it. Dominant males rarely are particularly aggressive, and those that are typically are on their way out: the ones that need to use it are often about to lose it. Instead, maintaining dominance requires social intelligence and impulse control -- the ability to form prudent coalitions, show some tolerance of subordinates, and ignore most provocations.

Recent work, moreover, has demonstrated that females have something to say about which males get to pass on their genes. The traditional view was based on a "linear access" model of reproduction: if one female is in heat, the alpha male gets to mate with her; if two are in heat, the alpha male and the second-ranking male get their opportunity; and so on. Yet we now know that female baboons are pretty good at getting away from even champions of male-male competition if they want to and can sneak off instead with another male they actually desire. And who would that be? Typically, it is a male that has followed a different strategy of building affiliative relations with the female -- grooming her a lot, helping to take care of her kids, not beating her up. These nice-guy males seem to pass on at least as many copies of their genes as their more aggressive peers, not least because they can go like this for years, without the life-shortening burnout and injuries of the gladiators.

And so the crude picture of combat as the sole path to evolutionary success is wrong. The average male baboon does opt for the combative route, but there are important phases of his life when aggression is less important than social intelligence and restraint, and there are evolutionarily fruitful alternative courses of action.

Even within the bare-knuckle world of male-male aggression, we are now recognizing some surprising outposts of primate civility. For one thing, primates can make up after a fight. Such reconciliation was first described by Frans de Waal, of Emory University, in the early 1980s; it has now been observed in some 27 different species of primates, including male chimps, and it works as it is supposed to, reducing the odds of further aggression between the two ex-combatants. And various primates, including male baboons, will sometimes cooperate, for example by supporting one another in a fight. Coalitions can involve reciprocity and even induce what appears to be a sense of justice or fairness. In a remarkable study by de Waal and one of his students, capuchin monkeys were housed in adjacent cages. A monkey could obtain food on its own (by pulling a tray of food toward its cage) or with help from a neighbor (by pulling a heavier tray together); in the latter case, only one of the monkeys was given access to the food in question. The monkeys that collaborated proved more likely to share it with their neighbor.

Even more striking are lifelong patterns of cooperation among some male chimps, such as those that form bands of brothers. Among certain primate species, all the members of one gender will leave their home troop around puberty, thus avoiding the possibility of genetically deleterious inbreeding. Among chimps, the females leave home, and as a result, male chimps typically spend their lives in the company of close male relatives. Animal behaviorists steeped in game theory spend careers trying to figure out how reciprocal cooperation gets started among nonrelatives, but it is clear that stable reciprocity among relatives emerges readily.

Thus, even the violent primates engage in reconciliation and cooperation -- but only up to a point. For starters, as noted in regard to the bonobo, there would be nothing to reconcile without violence and conflict in the first place. Furthermore, reconciliation is not universal: female savanna baboons are good at it, for example, but males are not. Most important, even among species and genders that do reconcile, it is not an indiscriminate phenomenon: individuals are more likely to reconcile with those who can be useful to them. This was demonstrated in a brilliant study by Marina Cords, of Columbia University, in which the value of some relationships among a type of macaque monkey was artificially raised. Animals were again caged next to each other under conditions in which they could obtain food by themselves or through cooperation, and those pairs that developed the capacity for cooperation were three times as likely to reconcile after induced aggression as noncooperators. Tension-reducing reconcilia-tion, in other words, is most likely to occur among animals who already are in the habit of cooperating and have an incentive to keep doing so.

Some deflating points emerge from the studies of cooperation as well, such as the fact that coalitions are notoriously unstable. In one troop of baboons I studied in the early 1980s, male-male coalitions lasted less than two days on average before collapsing, and most cases of such collapse involved one partner failing to reciprocate or, even more dramatically, defecting to the other side during a fight. Finally, and most discouraging, is the use to which most coalitions are put. In theory, cooperation could trump individualism in order to, say, improve food gathering or defend against predators. In practice, two baboons that cooperate typically do so in order to make a third miserable.

Goodall was the first to report the profoundly disquieting fact that bands of related male chimps carry out cooperative "border patrols" -- searching along the geographic boundary separating their group from another and attacking neighboring males they encounter, even to the point of killing other groups off entirely. In-group cooperation can thus usher in not peace and tranquility, but rather more efficient extermination.

So primate species with some of the most aggressive and stratified social systems have been seen to cooperate and resolve conflicts -- but not consistently, not necessarily for benign purposes, and not in a cumulative way that could lead to some fundamentally non-Hobbesian social outcomes. The lesson appears to be not that violent primates can transcend their natures, but merely that the natures of these species are subtler and more multifaceted than previously thought. At least that was the lesson until quite recently.

Old Primates and New Tricks

To some extent, the age-old "nature versus nurture" debate is silly. The action of genes is completely intertwined with the environment in which they function; in a sense, it is pointless to even discuss what gene X does, and we should consider instead only what gene X does in environment Y. Nonetheless, if one had to predict the behavior of some organism on the basis of only one fact, one might still want to know whether the most useful fact would be about genetics or about the environment.

The first two studies to show that primates were somewhat independent from their "natures" involved a classic technique in behavioral genetics called cross-fostering. Suppose some animal has engaged in a particular behavior for generations -- call it behavior A. We want to know if that behavior is due to shared genes or to a multigenerationally shared environment. Researchers try to answer the question by cross-fostering the animal, that is, switching the animal's mother at birth so that she is raised by one with behavior B, and then watching to see which behavior the animal displays when she grows up. One problem with this approach is that an animal's environment does not begin at birth -- a fetus shares a very intimate environment with its mother, namely the body's circulation, chock-full of hormones and nutrients that can cause lifelong changes in brain function and behavior. Therefore, the approach can be applied only asymmetrically: if a behavior persists in a new environment, one cannot conclude that genes are the cause, but if a behavior changes in a new environment, then one can conclude that genes are not the cause. This is where the two studies come in.

In the early 1970s, a highly respected primatologist named Hans Kummer was working in Ethiopia, in a region containing two species of baboons with markedly different social systems. Savanna baboons live in large troops, with plenty of adult females and males. Hamadryas baboons, in contrast, have a more complex, multilevel society. Because they live in a much harsher, drier region, hamadryas have a distinctive ecological problem. Some resources are singular and scarce -- like a rare watering hole or a good cliff face to sleep on at night in order to evade predators -- and large numbers of animals are likely to want to share them. Other resources, such as the vegetation they eat, are sparse and widely dispersed, requiring animals to function in small, separate groups. As a result, hamadryas have evolved a "harem" structure -- a single adult male surrounded by a handful of adult females and their children -- with large numbers of discrete harems converging, peacefully, for short periods at the occasional desirable watering hole or cliff face.

Kummer conducted a simple experiment, trapping an adult female savanna baboon and releasing her into a hamadryas troop and trapping an adult female hamadryas and releasing her into a savanna troop. Among hamadryas, if a male threatens a female, it is almost certainly this brute who dominates the harem, and the only way for the female to avoid injury is to approach him -- i.e., return to the fold. But among savanna baboons, if a male threatens a female, the way for her to avoid injury is to run away. In Kummer's experiment, the females who were dropped in among a different species initially carried out their species-typical behavior, a major faux pas in the new neighborhood. But gradually, they assimilated the new rules. How long did this learning take? About an hour. In other words, millennia of genetic differences separating the two species, a lifetime of experience with a crucial social rule for each female, and a miniscule amount of time to reverse course completely.

The second experiment was set up by de Waal and his student Denise Johanowicz in the early 1990s, working with two macaque monkey species. By any human standards, male rhesus macaques are unappealing animals. Their hierarchies are rigid, those at the top seize a disproportionate share of the spoils, they enforce this inequity with ferocious aggression, and they rarely reconcile after fights. Male stump tail macaques, in contrast, which share almost all of their genes with their rhesus macaque cousins, display much less aggression, more affiliative behaviors, looser hierarchies, and more egalitarianism.

Working with captive primates, de Waal and Johanowicz created a mixed-sex social group of juvenile macaques, combining rhesus and stump tails together. Remarkably, instead of the rhesus macaques bullying the stump tails, over the course of a few months, the rhesus males adopted the stump tails' social style, eventually even matching the stump tails' high rates of reconciliatory behavior. It so happens, moreover, that stump tails and rhesus macaques use different gestures when reconciling. The rhesus macaques in the study did not start using the stump tails' reconciliatory gestures, but rather increased the incidence of their own species-typical gestures. In other words, they were not merely imitating the stump tails' behavior; they were incorporating the concept of frequent reconciliation into their own social practices. When the newly warm-and-fuzzy rhesus macaques were returned to a larger, all-rhesus group, finally, their new behavioral style persisted.

This is nothing short of extraordinary. But it brings up one last question: When those rhesus macaques were transferred back into the all-rhesus world, did they spread their insights and behaviors to the others? Alas, they did not. For that, we need to move on to our final case.

Left Behind

In the early 1980s, "Forest Troop," a group of savanna baboons I had been studying -- virtually living with -- for years, was going about its business in a national park in Kenya when a neighboring baboon group had a stroke of luck: its territory encompassed a tourist lodge that expanded its operations and consequently the amount of food tossed into its garbage dump. Baboons are omnivorous, and "Garbage Dump Troop" was delighted to feast on leftover drumsticks, half-eaten hamburgers, remnants of chocolate cake, and anything else that wound up there. Soon they had shifted to sleeping in the trees immediately above the pit, descending each morning just in time for the day's dumping of garbage. (They soon got quite obese from the rich diet and lack of exercise, but that is another story.)

The development produced nearly as dramatic a shift in the social behavior of Forest Troop. Each morning, approximately half of its adult males would infiltrate Garbage Dump Troop's territory, descending on the pit in time for the day's dumping and battling the resident males for access to the garbage. The Forest Troop males that did this shared two traits: they were particularly combative (which was necessary to get the food away from the other baboons), and they were not very interested in socializing (the raids took place early in the morning, during the hours when the bulk of a savanna baboon's daily communal grooming occurs).

Soon afterward, tuberculosis, a disease that moves with devastating speed and severity in nonhuman primates, broke out in Garbage Dump Troop. Over the next year, most of its members died, as did all of the males from Forest Troop who had foraged at the dump.[See Footnote #1] The results were that Forest Troop was left with males who were less aggressive and more social than average and the troop now had double its previous female-to-male ratio.

The social consequences of these changes were dramatic. There remained a hierarchy among the Forest Troop males, but it was far looser than before: compared with other, more typical savanna

baboon groups, high-ranking males rarely harassed subordinates and occasionally even relinquished contested resources to them. Aggression was less frequent, particularly against third parties. And rates of affiliative behaviors, such as males and females grooming each other or sitting together, soared. There were even instances, now and then, of adult males grooming each other -- a behavior nearly as unprecedented as baboons sprouting wings.

This unique social milieu did not arise merely as a function of the skewed sex ratio; other primatologists have occasionally reported on troops with similar ratios but without a comparable social atmosphere. What was key was not just the predominance of females, but the type of male that remained. The demographic disaster -- what evolutionary biologists term a "selective bottleneck" -- had produced a savanna baboon troop quite different from what most experts would have anticipated.

But the largest surprise did not come until some years later. Female savanna baboons spend their lives in the troop into which they are born, whereas males leave their birth troop around puberty; a troop's adult males have thus all grown up elsewhere and immigrated as adolescents. By the early 1990s, none of the original low aggression/high affiliation males of Forest Troop's tuberculosis period was still alive; all of the group's adult males had joined after the epidemic. Despite this, the troop's unique social milieu persisted -- as it does to this day, some 20 years after the selective bottleneck. In other words, adolescent males that enter Forest Troop after having grown up elsewhere wind up adopting the unique behavioral style of the resident males. As defined by both anthropologists and animal behaviorists, "culture" consists of local behavioral variations, occurring for nongenetic and non-ecological reasons, that last beyond the time of their originators. Forest Troop's low aggression/high affiliation society constitutes nothing less than a multigenerational benign culture.

Continuous study of the troop has yielded some insights into how its culture is transmitted to newcomers. Genetics obviously plays no role, nor apparently does self-selection: adolescent males that transfer into the troop are no different from those that transfer into other troops, displaying on arrival similarly high rates of aggression and low rates of affiliation. Nor is there evidence that new males are taught to act in benign ways by the residents. One cannot rule out the possibility that some observational learning is occurring, but it is difficult to detect given that the distinctive feature of this culture is not the performance of a unique behavior but the performance of typical behaviors at atypically extreme rates.

To date, the most interesting hint about the mechanism of transmission is the way recently transferred males are treated by Forest Troop's resident females. In a typical savanna baboon troop, newly transferred adolescent males spend years slowly working their way into the social fabric; they are extremely low ranking -- ignored by females and noted by adult males only as convenient targets for aggression. In Forest Troop, by contrast, new male transfers are inundated with female attention soon after their arrival. Resident females first present themselves sexually to new males an average of 18 days after the males arrive, and they first groom the new males an average of 20 days after they arrive (normal savanna baboons introduce such behaviors after 63 and 78 days, respectively). Furthermore, these welcoming gestures occur more frequently in Forest Troop during the early post-transfer period, and there is four times as much grooming of males by females in Forest Troop as elsewhere. From almost the moment they arrive, in other words, new males find out that in Forest Troop, things are done differently.

At present, I think the most plausible explanation is that this troop's special culture is not passed on actively but simply emerges, facilitated by the actions of the resident members. Living in a group with half the typical number of males, and with the males being nice guys to boot, Forest Troop's females become more relaxed and less wary. As a result, they are more willing to take a chance and reach out socially to new arrivals, even if the new guys are typical jerky adolescents at first. The new males, in turn, finding themselves treated so well, eventually relax and adopt the behaviors of the troop's distinctive social milieu.

Natural Born Killers?

Are there any lessons to be learned here that can be applied to human-on-human violence -- apart, that is, from the possible desirability of giving fatal cases of tuberculosis to aggressive people?

Any biological anthropologist opining about human behavior is required by long-established tradition to note that for 99 percent of human history, humans lived in small, stable bands of related hunter-gatherers. Game theorists have shown that a small, cohesive group is the perfect setting for the emergence of cooperation: the identities of the other participants are known, there are opportunities for multiple iterations of games (and thus the ability to punish cheaters), and there is open-book play (players can acquire reputations). And so, those hunter-gatherer bands were highly egalitarian. Empirical and experimental data have also shown the cooperative advantages of small groups at the opposite human extreme, namely in the corporate world.

But the lack of violence within small groups can come at a heavy price. Small homogenous groups with shared values can be a nightmare of conformity. They can also be dangerous for outsiders. Unconsciously emulating the murderous border patrols of closely related male chimps, militaries throughout history have sought to form small, stable units; inculcate them with rituals of pseudokinship; and thereby produce efficient, cooperative killing machines.

Is it possible to achieve the cooperative advantages of a small group without having the group reflexively view outsiders as the Other? One way is through trade. Voluntary economic exchanges not only produce profits; they can also reduce social friction -- as the macaques demonstrated by being more likely to reconcile with a valued partner in food acquisition.

Another way is through a fission-fusion social structure, in which the boundaries between groups are not absolute and impermeable. The model here is not the multilevel society of the hamadryas baboons, both because their basic social unit of the harem is despotic and because their fusion consists of nothing more than lots of animals occasionally coming together to utilize a resource peacefully. Human hunter-gatherers are a better example to follow, in that their small bands often merge, split, or exchange members for a while, with such fluidity helping to solve not only environmental resource problems but social problems as well. The result is that instead of the all-or-nothing world of male chimps, in which there is only one's own group and the enemy, hunter-gatherers can enjoy gradations of familiarity and cooperation stretching over large areas.

The interactions among hunter-gatherers resemble those of other networks, where there are individual nodes (in this case, small groups) and where the majority of interactions between the nodes are local ones, with the frequency of interactions dropping off as a function of distance. Mathematicians have shown that when the ratios among short-, middle-, and long-distance interactions are optimal, networks are robust: they are dominated by highly cooperative clusters of local interactions, but they also retain the potential for less frequent, long-distance communication and coordination.

Optimizing the fission-fusion interactions of hunter-gatherer networks is easy: cooperate within the band; schedule frequent joint hunts with the next band over; have occasional hunts with bands somewhat farther out; have a legend of a single shared hunt with a mythic band at the end of the earth. Optimizing the fission-fusion interactions in contemporary human networks is vastly harder, but the principles are the same.

In exploring these subjects, one often encounters a pessimism built around the notion that humans, as primates, are hard-wired for xenophobia. Some brain-imaging studies have appeared to support this view in a particularly discouraging way. There is a structure deep inside the brain called the amygdala, which plays a key role in fear and aggression, and experiments have shown that when subjects are presented with a face of someone from a different race, the amygdala gets metabolically active -- aroused, alert, ready for action. This happens even when the face is presented "subliminally," which is to say, so rapidly that the subject does not consciously see it.

More recent studies, however, should mitigate this pessimism. Test a person who has a lot of experience with people of different races, and the amygdala does not activate. Or, as in a wonderful experiment by Susan Fiske, of Princeton University, subtly bias the subject beforehand to think of people as individuals rather than as members of a group, and the amygdala does not budge. Humans may be hard-wired to get edgy around the Other, but our views on who falls into that category are decidedly malleable.

In the early 1960s, a rising star of primatology, Irven DeVore, of Harvard University, published the first general overview of the subject. Discussing his own specialty, savanna baboons, he wrote that they "have acquired an aggressive temperament as a defense against predators, and aggressiveness cannot be turned on and off like a faucet. It is an integral part of the monkeys' personalities, so deeply rooted that it makes them potential aggressors in every situation." Thus the savanna baboon became, literally, a textbook example of life in an aggressive, highly stratified, male-dominated society. Yet within a few years, members of the species demonstrated enough behavioral plasticity to transform a society of theirs into a baboon utopia.

The first half of the twentieth century was drenched in the blood spilled by German and Japanese aggression, yet only a few decades later it is hard to think of two countries more pacific. Sweden spent the seventeenth century rampaging through Europe, yet it is now an icon of nurturing tranquility. Humans have invented the small nomadic band and the continental megastate, and have demonstrated a flexibility whereby uprooted descendants of the former can function effectively in the latter. We lack the type of physiology or anatomy that in other mammals determine their mating system, and have come up with societies based on monogamy, polygyny, and polyandry. And we have fashioned some religions in which violent acts are the entre to paradise and other religions in which the same acts consign one to hell. Is a world of peacefully coexisting human Forest Troops possible? Anyone who says, "No, it is beyond our nature," knows too little about primates, including ourselves.

[Footnote #1] Considerable sleuthing ultimately revealed that the disease had come from tainted meat in the garbage dump, which had been sold to the tourist lodge thanks to a corrupt meat inspector. The studies were the first of this kind of outbreak in a wild primate population and showed that, in contrast to what happens with humans and captive primates, there was little animal-to-animal transmission of the tuberculosis, and so the disease did not spread in Forest Troop beyond the garbage eaters.

Chapter 10

Early Hominids: Brief News and New Insights

Article A:
Lucy's Kind Takes Humanlike Turn
Bruce Bower

In a line of human ancestors that lived more than 3 million years ago, adult males were only around 15 percent larger than adult females, a new study finds. Such a moderate sex difference in Australopithecus afarensis suggests that males in the ancient species formed coalitions with each other and often established monogamous relationships with females just as do modern human males and those of other species with nearly equal-size sexes, say Philip L. Reno of Kent (Ohio) State University and his coworkers. A. afarensis is best known for the partial skeleton called Lucy round nearly 30 years ago in Ethiopia. Prior research indicated that A. afarensis males were substantially larger than females, as is the case for male gorillas and orangutans, which can be 50 percent larger than females. Such species typically feature a lot of fighting among males and frequent switching of sexual partners.

The size gap between genders closed for Lucy's kind when Reno's team used new statistical methods to estimate body proportions and identify sexes using fossils from more than 20 A. afarensis individuals. Skeletal analyses of people, chimpanzees, and gorillas indicated that the modest size difference between A. afarensis sexes matched that between the human sexes, the scientists report in an upcoming Proceedings of the National Academy of Sciences.

Article B
First Family's Last Stand
Bruce Bower

Nearly 30 years ago, excavations at Ethiopia's Hadar site yielded the 3.2-million-year-old hominid remains of nine adults and four children who apparently met a sudden, collective demise. Researchers have since speculated that this group, unearthed in a shallow channel and dubbed the First Family by its discoverers, either drowned during a flood or died after sinking into a mucky pit.

All the fossils belong to Australopithecus afarensis, the same species as the famous partial skeleton from Hadar called Lucy.

Renewed work at Hadar over the past decade has produced additional First Family fossils and inspired a revised theory of how these ancient folk perished. It now appears that at least 17 individuals, including three adolescents and five children, were killed in an attack by large predators, such as saber-tooth cats, say Anna K. Behrensmeyer of the Smithsonian Institution in Washington, D.C., and Elizabeth H. Harmon of Arizona State University in Tempe.

Behrensmeyer and Harmon first determined that the channel in which the First Family perished carried only a shallow stream of water, so they probably didn't drown. Next, the researchers determined that the First Family died in an isolated area that contains few remains of other creatures.

Finally, the First Family's fossils display a cardinal sign of carnivore consumption. Remains from below the head come primarily from the arms and legs, with virtually no rib or vertebral bones. Carcasses fed on first by large predators and then by smaller, scavenging animals commonly exhibit this pattern of bone loss, the researchers say.

Article C
Unified Erectus: Fossil Suggests Single Human Ancestor
J. Pickell

A newly found, million-year-old African skull is fueling an ongoing debate over whether Homo erectus was a single wide-ranging species or several localized ones. The skull appears similar to those found in Asia, suggesting that the populations were in fact one species.

Fossils of H. erectus were discovered in Java in the 1800s. For many years, this species was recognized as the sole link between humans' earliest direct ancestor, Homo habilis, and modern Homo sapiens. H. erectus emerged 1.8 million years ago and may have survived to times as recent as 50,000 years ago.

Beginning in the 1980s, with the advent of new methods of analysis, some anthropologists have argued for splitting up H. erectus (SN: 6/20/92, p. 408). Proponents of this argument hold that European and African specimens formerly considered H. erectus belong to another species that they call Homo ergaster. They say that H. ergaster evolved into modern man but the Asia-bound H. erectus came up against an evolutionary dead end.

Arguments have raged, with some scientists proposing that observed differences between specimens are due to evolution in a single species over time--most African fossils are older than Asian ones--rather than the presence of two distinct species.

The newfound specimen is younger than most African fossils assigned to H. ergaster and contemporary with some Asian H. erectus specimens, with which it shares striking similarities.

This is the first time that it's been possible to compare Asian and African fossils from the same period, says W. Henry Gilbert of the University of California, Berkeley, who discovered the fossil. The find may vindicate researchers who argued against dividing the species, he says.

The skull--which is missing the lower face, jaw, and teeth--comes from a fossil-rich region 140 miles northeast of Addis Ababa, Ethiopia. Scratch marks suggest that the individual may have been killed by a lion or hyena that ate the lower face and gnawed the skull in an attempt to extract the brain, says study coauthor Tim White, also of UC-Berkeley. Researchers spent 2 years cleaning the partially crushed skull.

With the new specimen in hand, White and his coworkers compared 14 groups of H. erectus and H. ergaster skulls from Asia, Africa, and Georgia, formerly in the Soviet Union. The researchers found a considerable overlap in shape between specimens from Asia and the other geographic regions, they report in the March 21 Nature. Features such as a short bulging forehead in the new fossil are similar to those in Asian H. erectus, says White.

Though most anthropologists are excited with the find, some disagree with the authors' conclusions. "The researchers should be congratulated on finding such a fantastic specimen," says Bernard Wood of George Washington University in Washington, D.C. However, they can't rule out that the new specimen is H. ergaster, he adds.

"I don't think this will conclude the debate," says Chris Stringer of the Natural History Museum in London. He points out that scientists who support dividing the species based many conclusions on dental features of H. erectus. These can't be compared with the new fossil because it's missing its teeth.

Others feel the fossil provides unequivocal evidence of a single species. "This slams the door shut [on the debate]," says C. Owen Lovejoy of Kent (Ohio) State University. "Now, all these specimens can be confidently restored to their original designation as H. erectus." "This find should put the issue to rest," agrees Milford Wolpoff of the University of Michigan in Ann Arbor. However, he adds, "no discovery ever seems to put things to rest in a field as contentious as paleontology."

Article D
Ancestral Split in Africa, China
Bruce Bower

Homo erectus, the species usually regarded as the precursor of Homo sapiens, developed markedly different forms of behavior and social organization in Africa and China, says David E. Hopwood of the State University of New York at Binghamton.

In eastern Africa, H. erectus fashioned increasingly complex and diverse stone tools from around 1.8 million to 300,000 years ago, Hopwood contends. Occupation sites grew more numerous throughout that time. Many of them were eventually separated by a distance of only 1 to 2 miles, reflecting the social networking that was needed to organize travels to distant outcroppings to retrieve stones suitable for tools, Hopwood says. In contrast, H. erectus artifacts found at sites in China from the same time span exhibit no substantial changes in tool-making. Chinese sites are far more distantly spaced on the landscape, indicating little contact between inhabitants of different locations.

Intense competition for food with large predators, in an environment subject to frequent changes, prompted African H. erectus groups to invent new tools and forge cooperative bonds, Hopwood theorizes. Relatively stable environmental conditions in China encouraged more consistency in tool-making among groups that had no need for regular interaction.

Chapter 11

Recent Hominids: Transformations in Anatomically Modern Forms

Article A
Gene Test Probes Neanderthal Origins
Bruce Bower

A technique for discerning the similarity of DNA specimens supports earlier genetic evidence that Neandertals were a dead-end species, a new study finds.

Neandertal DNA exhibits substantial genetic differences from the DNA of both ancient Homo sapiens and modern humans, reports a team led by Lutz Bachmann of the Field Museum in Chicago.

"These data support the hypothesis that Neandertals were not ancestors of anatomically modern [humans]," the scientists assert in the June AMERICAN JOURNAL OF HUMAN GENETICS.

Bachmann's team examined DNA from Neandertal fossils from between 110,000 and 50,000 years ago and a H. sapiens fossil from about 35,000 years ago.

The group relied on a standard method for comparing genomes. For each of the fossils, the researchers measured the extent to which the nuclear DNA chemically bonded to nuclear DNA

samples from the fossils, modern humans, and chimpanzees. Strong bonds between DNA samples signify a close evolutionary relationship.

Compared with the two Neandertal samples, DNA from the early H. sapiens fossil exhibited a markedly different pattern of binding strengths to the set of samples, the researchers say. Chimpanzee DNA, however, elicited roughly equal amounts of binding from the Neandertal, early H. sapiens, and modern-human DNA samples, they add.

Differences in the binding propensities of DNA from Neandertal and H. sapiens may reflect contrasts in the length of repeated nucleotide sequences between the species, the investigators theorize. The variations probably evolved rapidly, they argue.

Anthropologist Erik Trinkaus of Washington University in St. Louis views the new genetic findings as inconclusive regarding Neandertals' evolutionary status. This measure, he says, provides a rougher estimate of genetic similarity than studies that compare specific mitochondrial DNA nucleotide sequences of Neandertals and modern humans (SN: 2/6/99, p. 88).

"[Bachmann's group] used a crude measure of DNA differences," Trinkaus says. "How big of a genetic difference is needed to discriminate between two species?" he asks. "Answers to that question are very subjective."

Trinkaus argues that fossil evidence shows signs of considerable interbreeding between Neandertals and modern humans (SN: 5/8/99, p. 295). Genetic remnants of that interbreeding may have diminished enough over time to escape the notice of current DNA probes, he asserts.

Article B
When the Human Spirit Soared: Cultural Evolution Shifted into High Gear with the Appearance of Anatomically Modern Humans in the Late Ice Age
Bruce Bower

There is a cave in the French Pyrenees whose walls contain more than 200 human handprints dating to about 26,000 years ago. But there is something puzzling about the prehistoric prints: All except 10 have fingers missing. Some investigators have suggested that the missing fingers were hacked off in ritual mutilations. Others have argued that disease and infection destroyed the digits. One anthropologist proposed that the fingers only appear to be missing and were tucked into the palm of the hand, indicating that a kind of gestural language or code was involved.

Although the handprints were first described in 1963, the mystery of the missing fingers remains unsolved. Make no mistake; the people who brushed or blew pigment around their hands on the cave wall were just like us in body and brain. They participated in the rapid development of art and technology that began in the Upper Paleolithic, or late Ice Age, which extended from 35,000 to 12,000 years ago.

The perplexing handprints point to a larger archaeological problem: In an attempt to understand complex Upper Paleolithic cultures, scientists have only inanimate remains to work with. "For archaeologists encountering an Ice Age painted cave, there are no informants,' says anthropologist Randall White of New York University. "They have all been dead for thousands of years. Therefore, our head-scratching is bound to go on for some time.'

But in the past decade, important strides have been made in reconstructing the lives of the earliest Homo sapiens sapiens, or modern humans. An up-to-date picture of the human condition in Ice Age Europe was presented at a recent New York University symposium. The gathering of French and U.S. investigators was held in conjunction with the opening of an exhibition, "Dark Caves, Bright Visions: Life in Ice Age Europe,' at the American Museum of Natural History in New York City.

About 150,000 years ago, Neanderthals were the first members of the human lineage to inhabit the glacial landscapes frequented by reindeer, wooly mammoths and other cold-adapted species. In an overlapping period of a few thousand years at the beginning of the Upper Paleolithic, they were replaced in Europe by anatomically modern Cro-Magnon populations. A popular theory, says anthropologist Fred Smith of the University of Tennessee in Knoxville, suggests that modern humans emerged in Africa about 50,000 years ago and spread into Asia and Europe. They and the Neanderthals kept their distance and competed for limited resources; the Neanderthals lost and were driven to extinction.

Smith argues, however, that the Neanderthals were not brusquely shunted aside by the innovative, up-and-coming Cro-Magnons. There are signs, he says, suggesting that interbreeding took place Some skeletal features, such as a protrusion on the occipital bene of the skull, are found among both species. In addition, several of the earliest Upper Paleolithic sites in central and western Europe contain hunting tools that apparently derive from the crude flakes employed by Neanderthals and also suggest that some type of intermingling occurred.

Regardless of how the Neanderthals were replaced, it is generally accepted that the European transition to Cro-Magnons was established between 34,000 and 30,000 years ago. At that point, says White, rapid-fire advances in hunting technology and culture were set in motion. Flakes gave way to more finely honed blades used for hunting and cutting up carcasses. Music assumed an important role; the first known instrument, a bone flute found in France, dates to around 30,000 years ago.

By about 23,000 years ago, sewing needles made of bone debuted in southwestern France, allowing a more sophisticated tailoring of cold-weather clothes. Delicate-looking but deadly spear-throwers appeared 6,000 years later, often with animals carved or engraved on them.

"One of the most important developments of the Upper Paleolithic,' says White, "is the movement of goods, particularly items used for body decoration, across the landscape.' These include seashells, probably used on necklaces, that have been found at sites up to 100 miles from the ocean. Jewelry also incorporated stone and ivory beads and the teeth of dangerous animals, such as bears and lions.

The transport of these items was facilitated by European geography at the time, which, says White, was largely composed of grasslands rather than the arctic tundra one might expect.

The best-known portable art objects of the late Ice Age are so-called Venus figurines, typically small sculptures of women with the breasts and buttocks accentuated. Some anthropologists have suggested they were fertility images. Because Venus figurines have been found across a 3,000-mile swath from western to central Europe, researchers have also proposed that artistic styles and belief systems were passed on and maintained through interactions between groups of Ice Age people.

Similar "social networks' appear to have been in force in eastern Europe, according to anthropologist Olga Soffer of the University of Illinois in Urbana-Champaign. She and several Soviet scientists have studied 29 Upper Paleolithic "camps' on the central Russian plain covering a 100,000-square-mile area. After the glacial advance peaked 18,000 years ago, says Soffer, classic Venus figurines were replaced at these sites by more abstract female forms and an abundance of painted signs on mammoth bones and skulls.

At about the same time, explains Soffer, groups of 50 to 100 people appear to have spent winter months at camps on the floodplain, where they hunted mammoths and other animals. During warmer weather the groups moved to higher ground. Evidence for more complex structures and social organization has been found at northern cold-weather sites, she notes, which seem to have been distribution centers for shells and other ornamental objects that ended up at sites several hundred miles away. It was, she says, like "an early version of the Hudson Bay Company.'
To date, Soffer and her colleagues have located 12 sites with dwellings made of mammoth bone, including the site at Mezhirich in the Ukraine, which has structures containing up to 20 tons of the creatures' skeletal remains. As an example of the careful planning that went into construction, Soffer points to one dwelling that is composed of repeated sections of lower jawbones, long bones, scapulas and other skeletal parts.

"This appears to be an Upper Paleolithic example of monumental architecture that probably had some kind of ritual significance,' contends Soffer. She cautions, however, that it is not known whether hunter-gatherer groups occupied these camps one time only or in sequence and if early types of worship took place there.

Explanations are similarly in short supply, says White, for the explosion of creativity and art at the transition to the Upper Paleolithic after several million years of predominantly biological change in the human lineage. But the beautiful images of animals on cave walls in southwest France, northern Spain and several other areas continue to draw scientific examination. The most famous examples of cave art, such as Lascaux in France and Altamira in Spain, date to the time period between 18,000 and 11,000 years ago.

Cave art and other evidence of human occupation in the Americas up to 32,000 years ago also have been uncovered (SN: 6/28/86, p.405).

For about 20 years now, investigators have realized that European cave paintings and engravings were organized according to preconceived plans. "There is an elaborate organization of space in Upper Paleolithic caves,' says French archaeologist Denis Vialou of the Musee de I'Homme in Paris. Vialou has documented strong relationships between paint color, type of signs, species of animal, and location within the cave at a site in France. Cultural variations in these relationships are apparent at different caves, he adds.

Henri Delporte, inspector general of French museums, notes that late Ice Age people tended to draw animals that they did not eat. At the cave of La Vache, for instance, horses make up one-quarter of the paintings and less than 1 percent of the remains of hunted animals, while ibexes appear sparingly on the walls and are abundant in the remains.

This suggests to Delporte the existence of a complex symbol system passed from parent to child during the Upper Paleolithic. "If these drawings were only made as a record of hunting,' he contends, "it wasn't necessary to make them so elaborate and beautiful.'

Painting itself underwent marked advances in the late Ice Age, says anthropologist Margaret Conkey of the State University of New York at Binghamton. Early efforts, such as the brushing or blowing of pigment around a hand, were later replaced by more complex methods. At Lascaux, she

points out, pigments mixed with clays were applied to the wall and allowed to crystallize. This layer was then painted over to achieve desired color tones and effects. At the same time, different painting techniques were used at other caves.

"The process of making an object or piece of art may be part of its meaning,' says Conkey. "Perhaps [late Ice Age] wall and portable art were fundamentally different in purpose. We're only beginning to think about how to correct for our own cultural assumptions about what constituted art in the Upper Paleolithic.'

Article C
Early Hunters are Guilty as Charged
J. Pickrell

The spread of humanity around the world often coincided with extinctions of large animals. For example, when humans migrated to the Americas-- traditionally dated to 11,000 years ago-- around 135 mammalian species disappeared within a few hundred years. Similar extinctions occurred in Australia and on Pacific islands (SN: 12/4/99, p. 360). In New Zealand, roughly 40 bird species vanished within 5 centuries after the Maori arrived in the early 130Os.
Some scientists deny that people are to blame for these sorts of extinctions, pointing instead to such factors as climate change, says Trevor H. Worthy of Paleofaunal Surveys in Masterton, New Zealand. Even for those species

clearly decimated by humans, he says, it's hard to determine whether hunting, habitat destruction, or the introduction of pests such as rats contributed most to the demise.

To address this uncertainty, Worthy and his colleagues examined bird remains at Marfells Beach in New Zealand. The area contains skeletons that accumulated without human intervention over the past 1,800 years and the bones of birds that were hunted by the early Maori.

The researchers reasoned that if an over-abundance of bones from a given bird species shows up at a Maori site, compared with a wild habitat in the area, that would indicate that the Maori's favored the species for hunting.

In the March 7 Proceedings of the Royal Society of London B, Worthy and his colleagues report finding such patterns for some species. Many more of these preferentially hunted birds went extinct than did species not on the Maori menu. All birds, however, were exposed to habitat destruction and invasive pests.

"Our data show clearly that the animals that went extinct ... were preferentially hunted," says Worthy.

"It would be difficult to refute this extremely persuasive study," says John Alroy of the University of California, Santa Barbara. Understanding historical cases of human-mediated extinction puts people's current ability to threaten species in perspective, he adds. --J.P.

Chapter 12

Toward a New American Environmentalism

By Benjamin Benson

This is an essay derived from a series of lectures that were delivered to California environmental groups in 2004. The author links America's environmental future to its environmental prehistory. In addition, the author proposes a restructuring of the philosophical foundation of American culture and, by implication, that of other modern industrial cultures. The author has spent years working with Native peoples of California.

The encompassing environmental challenge that America now faces is that of trying to balance human activities with a sustainable habitat. At present we are failing not only to keep a healthy American landscape but we, and other Western industrial cultures, are now impacting the global ecology. This challenge, although now larger in scale, is not at all new to our land. Other cultures that once managed America also struggled with similar issues, albeit on a smaller regional basis. Fortunately for us it is possible to deconstruct some of America's environmental prehistory and gain insight into our own potential solutions.

Anthropology and archaeology have demonstrated that some Native American cultures failed to sustain their way of life while others could probably have survived indefinitely. Clearly the greatest environmental challenges are faced by cultures with agricultural economies. Farming forces greater production from the habitat and requires greater labor input from people. Farming is always linked to population increase and increasing fragility in the human relationship to the land. A

noteworthy prehistoric failure of an agriculturally based civilization is evident in the American Southwest. In the four corners region of Arizona, New Mexico, southern Colorado, and southern Utah, hundreds of Anasazi communities were abandoned about 1300 A.D. Some of the more famous of these are Chaco Canyon and Mesa Verde. Tourists from throughout the world come to marvel at the extraordinary architecture, sophisticated solar and lunar astronomy, and exquisite ceramic art that flourished in the Southwest. But Anasazi culture failed to sustain itself and it collapsed before the arrival of the Spanish. It is important to note that this collapse was not the result of foreign invasion, disease, or any single catastrophic event. Rather it was a systemic, internal collapse, a cultural inability to sustain a viable habitat that would support a large population.

A similar collapse is seen in the Mississippi valley where once there were great pyramids, walled towns, and large, calendrically designed earthworks that were part of a once successful farming culture. Like the Anasazi the prehistoric Mississippians had trade networks that spanned the continent with links to Mexico. But for all their greatness both of these prehistoric American civilizations failed to adequately address that same environmental challenge that we face today. In their demise, both civilizations failed to stem a destructive cultural momentum and they both abandoned their lavish homes. In the case of the Anasazi, the fall was brutal. People were killing and eating each other in the final days at Chaco Canyon.

This same downward trajectory toward cultural failure is also seen in Mesoamerican prehistoric civilizations. Archaeologists continue to investigate the collapse at Teotihuacan in the highlands of Mexico where a huge cultural development descended into violent self-destruction. Similarly the ancient Maya of the Mexican Yucatan, Belize, and Guatemala abandoned many dozens of ceremonial and population centers after periods of internal violence and environmental stress.

In spite of some regional catastrophes, other Native American cultures succeeded in balancing human needs with environmental sustainability. After the fall of the Anasazi, according to several of the author's friends at Hopi, Arizona, the *Hopitu* elders created a sustainable agricultural community in one of the most fragile environments in the America with no creeks, no rivers, or forests. Hopi is America's oldest religiously based collective of people who were assembled from a variety of linguistic groups. Five thousand *Hopitu* or *People of Peace* have managed to live in balance with their habitat with constant population levels for at least seven hundred years. The Hopi environmental management system is fascinating and it provides an important model for us.

Other sustainable cultures had nearly identical principles of achieving homeostasis with the habitat. Good cultural examples are the northern California Pomo and Miwok who could probably have survived indefinitely had the Euro-Americans not replaced Indian life-ways with a culture that had so little sense for the sacred in Nature at that time. Fortunately enough is known about successful Native American cultural ecology from these groups from which we may still gain knowledge. As we examine these systems of American Indian environmental management we must dismiss the popular but false idea that Indians lived in completely natural, unaltered habitats. That idea is not only false but it creates impossible goals that no culture has ever reached. All human cultures, even small-scale bands and triblets, always modify their habitat to suit their cultural needs. Pomo and Coast Miwok environmental success did not occur by keeping nature unaltered. These cultures modified their habitats in major ways while managing a sustainable environment in which they lived in homeostasis. The most dramatic example is the Pomo and Miwok annual burning of vast sectors of their ecosystem. In so doing they increased the meadowlands while decreasing the brushy chaparral vegetation as well as eliminating many juvenile trees. The burning also enhanced the forage for the deer and increased their populations. The burning made the northern California oak woodland into something akin to a giant park; clearly it was not an untouched wilderness.

In addition, Hopi, Pomo, and Miwok cultures imposed rigid limits on exploitation of the habitat. Planting for the Hopi and hunting and gathering for all three cultures was strictly regulated by elaborate systems of religious controls that limited how much of any resource could be exploited. These rules are still in place at Hopi. Violation of these traditional rules was seen as a moral infraction. At the same time, all three groups controlled their own population levels. Through customs of birth spacing, the use of botanical contraceptives, and religious restrictions on sexuality, they limited their own numbers. But it is very important to emphasize that these cultural limitations on habitat exploitation and population levels were not founded in worldview patterns that resemble Western scientific reasoning. Nor were these native systems consciously understood in an overt way. Rather these limitations were founded in religious and philosophical systems that were taught as a human moral reality. Those cultures that had such limiting measures were those that survived the longest in balance with their habitats.

In Hopi, Pomo, and Miwok cultures, people are taught to recognize a divine essence in every species in nature. Humanity is defined as merely a part of the sacred fabric of interconnected life, not more important than other living beings. Indian children are taught that other life forms must be respected and honored because they too share the divine force of existence. Humans are not the rulers set apart from the environment, but collectively they *are* the environment along with all other precious life. Native customs such as fasting and abstinence at certain times of the year are ways of honoring the sacred essence of nature. Such sacrifices are part of ceremonies that honor nature's gifts with blessings. In the native view, to ignore and dishonor nature will result in eventual destruction of the individual and of society. Sufficient proof of this wisdom is obvious in the failure of the Anasazi, the Mississippians, Teotihuacan, and the classic Maya.

Native American philosophical beliefs that integrate humanity with nature are deeply imbedded cultural values that are expressed in spiritual and religious ritual. The Hopi farmer blesses the earth and sings to the plants in the most heartfelt ceremonial manner. In many native cultures, Indian hunters formally ask the animals to give themselves as sustenance for one's family. The hunter feels obligated to observe cultural restrictions when taking these precious gifts. Likewise the weaver must sing to the basket plants that have been nurtured by generations of weavers in her family. Native American environmental management is not founded in conscious, scientifically based behavior. Instead, ongoing cultural success occurs as a form of natural selection of the most adaptive cultures. Those cultures that last for millennia are those in which people internalize appropriate values and where they practice religiously based limitations on exploitation. Environmentally successful native cultures view nature animistically and engage in a social relationship with other creatures that share their world. Cultures who did not create religiously based systems of limitation often left ruins for later visitors to examine. One Second Mesa kiva priest with the simple words powerfully summarized the Hopi view: "Our way is about *respect*."

When millions of Europeans escaped failing Old World cultures to immigrate to the new "Americas," they ignored some of their life ways that might have given them examples of sustainability. They transplanted many doomed cultural traditions to North America and created their own myth of the limitless possibilities for exploitation of the new land. Perhaps America might now be more ready to assimilate what could have been known before? If native traditions were to be the model, it would require nothing less than a new definition of what it means to be a human being. Consumerism would be replaced with an environmentalism linked to a moral and religious foundation. To follow early native examples, nature must again be granted sacred status. In this context, current behaviors such as clear-cutting a forest habitat or ruining a creek ecosystem would be condemned as unholy.

One of the greatest difficulties for a moral and religious environmentalism to be formed in our time might be the combined resistance from the existing philosophical foundations of consumer culture and its established conservative religious authorities. The religious traditions of the industrial world have often worked to suppress or destroy cultures where nature is seen as an expression of the divine. A departure from current historic dogma and lessening of institutionalized religious power could be perceived as evil by some religious authorities. In one early California example, Junipero Serra saw native nature worship as evil and helped destroy dozens of sustainable cultures.

Ironically, viewing nature as sacred may be the most simple and effective means for the rebirth of sustainability that America now needs and to suggest this is not an attempt to delegitimize established religious thought. Nor is it a recommendation to usurp the traditions of particular native groups, who may regard that as exploitation. This shift in worldview is better seen as a reappraisal and redirection of often suppressed features of major religions. Knowledgeable religious scholars know that by sifting through established texts (Christian, Jewish, Muslim, Hindu, and Buddhist), one can find and embrace a new environmentalism and counter more conservative factions in their traditions. The opportunities for such study and action are many and varied. From a religious perspective, creation is the greatest miracle of all and it is the most immediate and accessible evidence of the divine. Religion, like all aspects of human culture constantly evolves. It is not difficult to begin an emphasis on many great sages as environmental prophets who did the work of the divine by advocating respect for creation. Jesus could be among them and it should be especially easy for Judaism, Hinduism, Buddhism and Taoism to find many similar voices and shift emphasis slightly to recapture their established environmental teachings.

From even this brief examination of native traditions, it appears critical for American environmentalism and for the world, to examine a revitalization of our religious and moral foundations in regard to nature. It seems clear that a new religious environmental emphasis and an alternative set of moral values that mute consumerism could foster and aid a new environmental sustainability.

With a new/ancient definition of what it means to be a human linked to such beliefs, rampant habitat destruction would become "sinful." If a *sacred* American landscape can be saved, perhaps these ethics could be shared in the farther reaches of the earth and a beautiful balance achieved once again.

Chapter 13

Did early man turn the outback into a barren desert?

Kate Ravilous

Once upon a time, Australia had a lush, green interior where grazing animals roamed, shrubs grew and the rain fell. Then, about 55,000 years ago, man arrived and started hunting the animals and burning the vegetation; ultimately, he drove the rain away and turned Australia's interior into the harsh, red, desert landscape that we see today.

There is no doubt that Australia's environment and climate has changed dramatically, but was man responsible? Gifford Miller, from the University of Colorado at Boulder, thinks so, and he and his colleagues have discovered convincing evidence to back up their theory.

The story starts at Lake Eyre, a huge salt flat covering one-sixth of Australia's landmass. Miller has been working with John Magee, of the Australian National University in Canberra, to drill down through the layers of mud, sand and salt at the site to uncover Lake Eyre's past. Going back 125,000 years, they have found that it used to be a vast freshwater lake, covering 35,000 square kilometers - an area the size of Taiwan. Rains used to swell the lake every year, following the patterns of the Australian monsoon. Then, about 14,000 years ago, "the monsoon stopped penetrating into the interior of Australia and Lake Eyre started to turn into a salt lake, like it is

today," says Miller.

While he was looking for reasons as to why the monsoon could have failed, Miller discovered that the Australian environment had suffered other dramatic changes in the past. "About 50,000 years ago, some 60 diffe
rent species of animal went extinct," he says. Miller's work focused on the demise of an ostrich-sized flightless bird called Genyornis newtoni. Measuring amino acids in the fossil eggshells of these birds and using radiocarbon dating, Miller and his colleagues found that Genyornis suddenly disappeared about 50,000 years ago. Meanwhile, other scientists have recorded that a host of other creatures, including a giant horned tortoise (the size of a small car) and a hippopotamus-sized relative of the wombat, were also snuffed out.

And animals were not the only ones to suffer. Pollen records suggest that many species of tree also vanished at this point. "Some of the most fire-sensitive plants, such as rainforest gymnosperms [plants whose seeds are not encased and thus protected from fire], disappear and never come back," says Miller. The evidence was circumstantial, but Miller became suspicious that all these sudden environmental changes were linked. He believes that early man may have pushed the natural balance too far by burning large areas of vegetation on a regular basis. The burning was probably used to hunt animals, promote new plant growth and exchange signals, but eventually it changed the environment irreparably. As well as burning plants and forcing animals to extinction, Miller thinks that man may be indirectly responsible for the monsoon failure - by removing the vegetation that sucked the rain into Australia's interior.

Miller and his colleagues have been looking at the link between Australia's vegetation and its climate, and using climate models to better understand the pattern of Australia's monsoons. Matching up pollen records with the Lake Eyre data has indicated that vegetation and climate used to be strongly linked. "Prior to 50,000 years ago, the vegetation beat to the same rhythm as the monsoon," says Miller. The lake data shows that Australia's monsoons followed processional cycles, related to the tilting of the Earth as it spins on its axis. Over a 22,000-year period, the Australian monsoon swung from being a deluge to a drizzle and back again. Similarly, the vegetation swung from being dominated by lush rainforest to being made up of higher proportions of shrubby plants and grass, and back again.

"The earliest humans arrived in Australia about 55,000 years ago, at the tail end of one of the stronger monsoon periods. There would have been lots of animals and plenty of green plants," says Miller. But that didn't last. By 45,000 years ago, Lake Eyre sediments show that the monsoon entered its weaker phase and became more of a dribble. At the same time, the Earth entered an ice age, making the planet cold and dry. It wasn't until about 14,000 years ago that the ice retreated and the monsoon rains started again. But, unlike on previous occasions, the strong monsoon rains never returned to the Australian interior. "We would have expected the climate to stay quite dry until about 14,000 years ago, but then the heavy monsoon should have reappeared," says Miller. Instead, the Lake Eyre sediments show that the interior of Australia continued to remain dry.

Using general circulation models (GCMs - climate simulators), Miller and his colleagues have been testing how sensitive the Australian monsoon is to changes in vegetation. They have found that plants appear to be the key to holding on to monsoon rainfall. When the model is run with vegetation covering the Australian interior, it gets twice the rainfall compared with a model run with no vegetation. "The GCM suggests that rainfall in the interior would be about 600mm per year when trees and plants cover the ground, compared with about 300mm per year when the ground is bare," Miller says.

Vegetation is likely to be important because it helps to recycle the rain via evaporation and transpiration. "Plants collect moisture and hold onto it. Without any vegetation the rain either evaporates, or sinks into the ground and disappears," explains Miller. Trees also add "surface roughness" to a landscape, which is thought to promote convection and to encourage rain-cloud formation. If Australia's earliest human inhabitants burnt enough vegetation, Miller believes that this could have tipped the balance and prevented the monsoon rains from reaching the interior.

Today, northern Australia still receives an annual monsoon, dousing cities like Darwin with more than 1,600mm of rain a year. The GCM models have shown that Australia's monsoon is connected to the northern-hemisphere climate and the Asian monsoon. "Early man didn't have enough influence to affect the global monsoon pattern, but it appears that localized burning was enough to produce a continental-scale change in the water balance and climate," says Miller.

It is unlikely that we can turn the clock back for Australia. In principle, trees could be planted to entice the moisture back, but thousands of years of desert weathering has left Australian soil very low in nutrients, making it almost impossible for trees to get a grasp again. "Physics is working against us right now. Perhaps we could try planting in another 11,000 years, when we are in a strong monsoon period again," says Miller.

If Miller and his colleagues are right about Australia's past, it provides a sobering lesson. Rainforest is being felled all over the world at an unprecedented rate and ecosystems pushed way out of kilter. What kind of effect will this have on the world's climate? Are we leaving a legacy to future generations of desert landscapes and unpredictable rainfall?

How prehistoric farmers saved us from new Ice Age

Robin McKie

Ancient man saved the world from a new Ice Age. That is the startling conclusion of climate researchers who say man-made global warming is not a modern phenomenon and has been going on for thousands of years.

Prehistoric farmers who slashed down trees and laid out the first rice paddies and wheat fields triggered major alterations to levels of greenhouse gases such as methane and carbon dioxide in the atmosphere, they say.

As a result, global temperatures - which were slowly falling around 8,000 years ago - began to rise. 'Current temperatures would be well on the way toward typical glacial temperatures, had it not been for the greenhouse gas contributions from early farming practices,' says Professor William Ruddiman of Virginia University.

The theory, based on studies of carbon dioxide and methane samples taken from Antarctic ice cores, is highly controversial - a point acknowledged by Ruddiman. 'Global warming skeptics could cite my work as evidence that human-generated greenhouse gases played a beneficial role for several thousand years by keeping the Earth's climate more hospitable than it would otherwise have been,' he states in the current issue of Scientific American

'However, others might counter that, if so few humans with relatively primitive technologies were able to alter the course of climate so significantly, then we have reason to be concerned about the current rise of greenhouse gases to unparalleled concentrations at unprecedented rates.'

Elaborating on his theory, Ruddiman said: 'Rice paddies flooded by irrigation generate methane for the same reason that natural wetlands do - vegetation decomposes in the stagnant water. Methane is also released as farmers burn grasslands,' Ruddiman points out.

Similarly, the cutting down of forests had a major effect. 'Whether the fallen trees were burnt or left to rot, their carbon would soon have been oxidized and ended up in the atmosphere as carbon dioxide.'

Computer models of the climate made by scientists at the University of Wisconsin-Madison suggest this rise in carbon dioxide and methane would have had a profound effect on Earth: without man's intervention, our planet would be 2C cooler than it is now, and spreading ice caps and glaciers would affect much of the world.

The idea that ancient farming may have had an impact on Earth's climate was given a cautious welcome by Professor Paul Valdes, an expert on ancient climate change based at Bristol University.

This is a very interesting idea,' he told The Observer. 'However, there are other good alternative explanations to explain the fluctuations that we see in temperature and greenhouse gas levels at this time. For example, other gases interact with methane and carbon dioxide in the atmosphere and changes in levels of these could account for these increases in greenhouse gases.'

Chapter 15

The Challenges We Face

Jeffrey Kluger and Andrea Dorfman

For starters, let's be clear about what we mean by "saving the earth." The globe doesn't need to be saved by us, and we couldn't kill it if we tried. What we do need to save—and what we have done a fair job of bollixing up so far—is the earth as we like it, with its climate, air, water and biomass all in that destructible balance that best supports life as we have come to know it. Muck that up, and the planet will simply shake us off, as it's shaken off countless species before us. In the end, then, it's us we're trying to save—and while the job is doable, it won't be easy.

The 1992 Earth Summit in Rio de Janeiro was the last time world leaders assembled to look at how to heal the ailing environment. Now, 10 years later, Presidents and Prime Ministers are convening at the World Summit on Sustainable Development in Johannesburg next week to reassess the planet's condition and talk about where to go from here. In many ways, things haven't changed: the air is just as grimy in many places, the oceans just as stressed, and most treaties designed to do something about it lie in incomplete states of ratification or implementation. Yet we're oddly smarter than we were in Rio. If years of environmental false starts have taught us anything, it's that it's time to quit seeing the job of cleaning up the world as a zero-sum game between industrial progress on the one hand and a healthy planet on the other. The fact is, it's development—well-planned, well-executed sustainable development—that may be what saves our bacon before it's too late.

Food
As we try to nourish 6 billion people, both bioengineering and organic farming will help

As the summiteers gather in Johannesburg, TIME is looking ahead to what the unfolding century—a green century—could be like. In this special report, we will examine several avenues to a healthier future, including green industry, green architecture, green energy, green transportation and even a greener approach to wilderness preservation. All of them have been explored before, but never so urgently as now. What gives such endeavors their new credibility is the hope and notion of sustainable development, a concept that can be hard to implement but wonderfully simple to understand.

Population
The tide of people may not ebb until the head count hits the 11 billion mark

With 6.1 billion people relying on the resources of the same small planet, we're coming to realize that we're drawing from a finite account. The amount of crops, animals and other biomatter we extract from the earth each year exceeds what the planet can replace by an estimated 20%, meaning it takes 14.4 months to replenish what we use in 12—deficit spending of the worst kind. Sustainable development works to reverse that, to expand the resource base and adjust how we use it so we're living off biological interest without ever touching principal. "The old environmental movement had a reputation of elitism," says Mark Malloch Brown, administrator of the United Nations Development Program (UNDP). "The key now is to put people first and the environment second, but also to remember that when you exhaust resources, you destroy people." With that in mind, the summiteers will wrestle with a host of difficult issues that affect both people and the environment. Among them:

• POPULATION AND HEALTH: While the number of people on earth is still rising rapidly, especially in the developing countries of Asia, the good news is that the growth rate is slowing. World population increased 48% from 1975 to 2000, compared with 64% from 1950 to 1975. As this gradual deceleration continues, the population is expected to level off eventually, perhaps at 11 billion sometime in the last half of this century.

Though it's not easy to see it from the well-fed West, a third of the world goes hungry

Economic-development and family-planning programs have helped slow the tide of people, but in some places, population growth is moderating for all the wrong reasons. In the poorest parts of the world, most notably Africa, infectious diseases such as AIDs, malaria, cholera and tuberculosis are having a Malthusian effect. Rural-land degradation is pushing people into cities, where crowded, polluted living conditions create the perfect breeding grounds for sickness. Worldwide, at least 68 million are expected to die of AIDs by 2020, including 55 million in sub-Saharan Africa. While any factor that eases population pressures may help the environment, the situation would be far less tragic if rich nations did more to help the developing world reduce birth rates and slow the spread of disease.

Efforts to provide greater access to family planning and health care have proved effective. Though women in the poorest countries still have the most children, their collective fertility rate is 50% lower than it was in 1969 and is expected to decline more by 2050. Other programs targeted at women include basic education and job training. Educated mothers not only have a stepladder out of poverty, but they also choose to have fewer babies.

Rapid development will require good health care for the young since there are more than 1 billion people ages 15 to 24. Getting programs in place to keep this youth bubble healthy could make it the most productive generation ever conceived. Says Thoraya Obaid, executive director of the U.N. Population Fund: "It's a window of opportunity to build the economy and prepare for the future."

• FOOD: Though it's not always easy to see it from the well-fed West, up to a third of the world is in danger of starving. Two billion people lack reliable access to safe, nutritious food, and 800 million of them—including 300 million children—are chronically malnourished.

Agricultural policies now in place define the very idea of unsustainable development. Just 15 cash crops such as corn, wheat and rice provide 90% of the world's food, but planting and replanting the same crops strips fields of nutrients and makes them more vulnerable to pests. Slash-and-burn planting techniques and overreliance on pesticides further degrade the soil.

Solving the problem is difficult, mostly because of the ferocious debate over how to do it. Biotech partisans say the answer lies in genetically modified crops—foods engineered for vitamins, yield and robust growth. Environmentalists worry that fooling about with genes is a recipe for Frankensteinian disaster. There is no reason, however, that both camps can't make a contribution.

Better crop rotation and irrigation can help protect fields from exhaustion and erosion. Old-fashioned cross-breeding can yield plant strains that are heartier and more pest-resistant. But in a world that needs action fast, genetic engineering must still have a role—provided it produces suitable crops. Increasingly, those crops are being created not just by giant biotech firms but also by home-grown groups that know best what local consumers need.

The National Agricultural Research Organization of Uganda has developed corn varieties that are more resistant to disease and thrive in soil that is poor in nitrogen. Agronomists in Kenya are developing a sweet potato that wards off viruses. Also in the works are drought-tolerant, disease-defeating and vitamin-fortified forms of such crops as sorghum and cassava—hardly staples in the West, but essentials elsewhere in the world. The key, explains economist Jeffrey Sachs, head of Columbia University's Earth Institute, is not to dictate food policy from the West but to help the developing world build its own biotech infrastructure so it can produce the things it needs the most. "We can't presume that our technologies will bail out poor people in Malawi," he says. "They need their own improved varieties of sorghum and millet, not our genetically improved varieties of wheat and soybeans."

Water
In 25 years two-thirds of humanity may live in nations running short of life's elixir

• WATER: For a world that is 70% water, things are drying up fast. Only 2.5% of water is fresh, and only a fraction of that is accessible. Meanwhile, each of us requires about 50 quarts per day for drinking, bathing, cooking and other basic needs. At present, 1.1 billion people lack access to clean drinking water and more than 2.4 billion lack adequate sanitation. "Unless we take swift and decisive action," says U.N. Secretary-General Kofi Annan, "by 2025, two-thirds of the world's population may be living in countries that face serious water shortages."

Only 2.5% of water is fresh, and only a fraction of that is accessible

The answer is to get smart about how we use water. Agriculture accounts for about two-thirds of the fresh water consumed. A report prepared for the summit thus endorses the "more crop per drop" approach, which calls for more efficient irrigation techniques, planting of drought- and salt-tolerant crop varieties that require less water and better monitoring of growing conditions, such as soil humidity levels. Improving water-delivery systems would also help, reducing the amount that is lost en route to the people who use it.

One program winning quick support is dubbed WASH—for Water, Sanitation and Hygiene for All—a global effort that aims to provide water services and hygiene training to everyone who lacks them by 2015. Already, the U.N., 28 governments and many nongovernmental organizations (NGOs) have signed on.

Climate
Car exhaust is a major source of the heat-trapping gases that produce global warming

• ENERGY AND CLIMATE: In the U.S., people think of rural electrification as a long-ago legacy of the New Deal. In many parts of the world, it hasn't even happened yet. About 2.5 billion people have no access to modern energy services, and the power demands of developing economies are expected to grow 2.5% per year. But if those demands are met by burning fossil fuels such as oil, coal and gas, more and more carbon dioxide and other greenhouse gases will hit the atmosphere. That, scientists tell us, will promote global warming, which could lead to rising seas, fiercer storms, severe droughts and other climatic disruptions.

Of more immediate concern is the heavy air pollution caused in many places by combustion of wood and fossil fuels. A new U.N. Environment Program report warns of the effects of a haze across all southern Asia. Dubbed the "Asian brown cloud" and estimated to be 2 miles thick, it may be responsible for hundreds of thousands of deaths a year from respiratory diseases.

The better way to meet the world's energy needs is to develop cheaper, cleaner sources. Pre-Johannesburg proposals call for eliminating taxation and pricing systems that encourage oil use and replacing them with policies that provide incentives for alternative energy. In India there has been a boom in wind power because the government has made it easier for entrepreneurs to get their hands on the necessary technology and has then required the national power grid to purchase the juice that wind systems produce.

Other technologies can work their own little miracles. Micro-hydroelectric plants are already operating in numerous nations, including Kenya, Sri Lanka and Nepal. The systems divert water from streams and rivers and use it to run turbines without complex dams or catchment areas. Each plant can produce as much as 200 kilowatts—enough to electrify 200 to 500 homes and businesses—and lasts 20 years. One plant in Kenya was built by 200 villagers, all of whom own shares in the cooperative that sells the power.

The Global Village Energy Partnership, which involves the World Bank, the UNDP and various donors, wants to provide energy to 300 million people, as well as schools, hospitals and clinics in 50,000 communities worldwide over 10 years. The key will be to match the right energy source to the right users. For example, solar panels that convert sunlight into electricity might be cost-effective in remote areas, while extending the power grid might be better in Third World cities.

Biodiversity
Unless we guard wilderness, as many as half of all species could vanish in this century

• BIODIVERSITY: More than 11,000 species of animals and plants are known to be threatened with extinction, about a third of all coral reefs are expected to vanish in the next 30 years and about 36 million acres of forest are being razed annually. In his new book, *The Future of Life*, Harvard biologist Edward O. Wilson writes of his worry that unless we change our ways half of all species could disappear by the end of this century.

Once you tear out swaths of ecosystem, you harm areas you didn't want to touch

The damage being done is more than aesthetic. Many vanishing species provide humans with both food and medicine. What's more, once you start tearing out swaths of ecosystem, you upset the existing balance in ways that harm even areas you didn't intend to touch. Environmentalists have said this for decades, and now that many of them have tempered ecological absolutism with developmental realism, more people are listening.

The Equator Initiative, a public-private group, is publicizing examples of sustainable development in the equatorial belt. Among the projects already cited are one to help restore marine fisheries in Fiji and another that promotes beekeeping as a source of supplementary income in rural Kenya. The Global Conservation Trust hopes to raise $260 million to help conserve genetic material from plants for use by local agricultural programs. "When you approach sustainable development from an environmental view, the problems are global," says the U.N.'s Malloch Brown. "But from a development view, the front line is local, local, local."

If that's the message environmental groups and industry want to get out, they appear to be doing a good job of it. Increasingly, local folks act whether world political bodies do or not. California Governor Gray Davis signed a law last month requiring automakers to cut their cars' carbon emissions by 2009.

Many countries are similarly proactive. Chile is encouraging sustainable use of water and electricity; Japan is dangling financial incentives before consumers who buy environmentally sound cars; and tiny Mauritius is promoting solar cells and discouraging use of plastics and other disposables.

Business is getting right with the environment too. The Center for Environmental Leadership in Business, based in Washington, is working with auto and oil giants including Ford, Chevron, Texaco and Shell to draft guidelines for incorporating biodiversity conservation into oil and gas exploration. And the center has helped Starbucks develop purchasing guidelines that reward coffee growers whose methods have the least impact on the environment. Says Nitin Desai, secretary-general of the Johannesburg summit: "We're hoping that partnerships—involving governments, corporations, philanthropies and NGOs—will increase the credibility of the commitment to sustainable development."

Will that happen? In 1992 the big, global measures of the Rio summit seemed like the answer to what ails the world. In 2002 that illness is—in many respects—worse. But if Rio's goal was to stamp out the disease of environmental degradation, Johannesburg's appears to be subtler—and perhaps better: treating the patient a bit at a time, until the planet as a whole at last gets well.

From *Time*, August 26, 2002, pp. A6–A12. © 2002 by Time Inc. Reprinted by permission.

Chapter 16

Lessons from Lost Worlds

Jared Diamond

Children have a wonderful ability to focus their parents' attention on the essentials. Before our twin sons were born in 1987, I had often heard about all the environmental problems projected to come to a head toward the middle of this century. But I was born in 1937, so I would surely be dead before 2050. Hence I couldn't think of 2050 as a real date, and I couldn't grasp that the environmental risks were real.

After the birth of our kids, my wife and I proceeded to obsess about the things most parents obsess about-schools, our wills, life insurance. Then I realized with a jolt: my kids will reach my present age of 65 in 2052. That's a real date, not an unimaginable one! My kids' lives will depend on the state of the world in 2052, not just on our decisions about life insurance and schools.

I should have known that. Having lived in Europe for years, I saw that the lives of my friends also born in 1937 had been affected greatly by the state of the world around them. For many of those overseas contemporaries growing up during World War II, that state of the world left them orphaned or homeless. Their parents may have thought wisely about life insurance, but their parents' generation had not thought wisely about world conditions. Over the heads of our own children now hang other threats from world conditions, different from the threats of 1939-45.

While the risk of nuclear war between major powers still exists, it's less acute now than 15 years ago, thank God. Many people worry about terrorists, and so do I, but then I reflect that terrorists could at worst kill "only" a few tens of millions of us. The even graver environmental problems that could do in all our children are environmental ones, such as global warming and land and water degradation.

These threats interact with terrorism by breeding the desperation that drives some individuals to become terrorists and others to support terrorists. Sept. 11 made us realize that we are not immune from the environmental problems of any country, no matter how remote-not even those of Somalia and Afghanistan. Of course, in reality, that was true before Sept. 11, but we didn't think much about it then. We and the Somalis breathe and pollute the same atmosphere, are bathed by the same oceans and compete for the same global pie of shrinking resources. Before Sept. 11, though, we thought of globalization as mainly meaning "us" sending "them" good things, like the Internet and Coca-Cola . Now we understand that globalization also means "them" being in a position to send "us" bad things, like terrorist attacks, emerging diseases, illegal immigrants and situations requiring the dispatch of U.S. troops.

A historical perspective can help us, because ours is not the first society to face environmental challenges. Many past societies collapsed partly from their failure to solve problems similar to those we face today--especially problems of deforestation, water management, topsoil loss and climate change. The long list of victims includes the Anasazi in the U.S. Southwest, the Maya, Easter Islanders, the Greenland Norse,

Mycenaean Greeks and inhabitants of the Fertile Crescent, the Indus Valley, Great Zimbabwe and Angkor Wat. The outcomes ranged from "just" a collapse of society, to the deaths of most people, to (in some cases) everyone's ending up dead. What can we learn from these events? I see four main sets of lessons.

First, environmental problems can indeed cause societies to collapse, even societies assaulting their environments with stone tools and far lower population densities than we have today.

Second, some environments are more fragile than others, making some societies more prone to collapse than others. Fragility varies even within the same country: for instance, some parts of the U.S., including Southern California, where I live, are especially at risk from low rainfall and salinization of soil from agriculture that is dependent on irrigation-the same problems that overwhelmed the Anasazi. Some nations occupy more fragile environments than do others. It's no accident that a list of the world's most environmentally devastated and/or overpopulated countries resembles a list of the world's current political tinderboxes. Both lists include Afghanistan, Haiti, Iraq, Nepal, Rwanda and Somalia.

Third, otherwise robust societies can be dragged down by the environmental problems of their trade partners. About 500 years ago, two Polynesian societies, on Henderson Island and Pitcairn Island, vanished because they depended for vital imports on the Polynesian society of Mangareva Island, which collapsed from deforestation. We Americans can well understand that outcome, having seen how vulnerable we are to instability in oil-exporting countries of the Middle East.

Fourth, we wonder, Why didn't those peoples see the problems developing around them and do something to avoid disaster? (Future generations may ask that question about us.) One explanation is the conflicts between the short-

term interests of those in power and the long-term interests of everybody: chiefs were becoming rich from processes that ultimately undermined society. That too is an acute issue today, as wealthy Americans do things that enrich themselves in the short run and harm everyone in the long run. As the Anasazi chiefs found, they could get away with those policies for a while, but ultimately they bought themselves the privilege of being merely the last to starve.

Of course, there are differences between our situation and those of past societies. Our problems are more dangerous than those of the Anasazi. Today there are far more humans alive, packing far greater destructive power, than ever before. Unlike the Anasazi, a society today can't collapse without affecting societies far away. Because of globalization, the risk we face today is of a worldwide collapse, not just a local tragedy.

People often ask if I am an optimist or a pessimist about our future. I answer that I'm cautiously optimistic. We face big problems that will do us in if we don't solve them. But we are capable of solving them. The risk we face isn't that of an asteroid collision beyond our ability to avoid. Instead our problems are of our own making, and so we can stop making them. The only thing lacking is the necessary political will.

The other reason for my optimism is the big advantage we enjoy over the Anasazi and other past societies: the power of the media. When the Anasazi were collapsing in the U.S. Southwest, they had no idea that Easter Island was also on a downward spiral thousands of miles away, or that Mycenaean Greece had collapsed 2,400 years earlier. But we know from the media what is happening all around the world, and we know from archaeologists what happened in the past. We can learn from that understanding of remote places and times; the Anasazi didn't have that option. Knowing history, we are not doomed to repeat it.

Reprinted with permission from *Time*, August 26, 2002, Vol. 160, Issue 9, p. A54.

EXERCISES
AND
MAP QUIZES

Map Quiz #1 - Locate the following items on the world map.

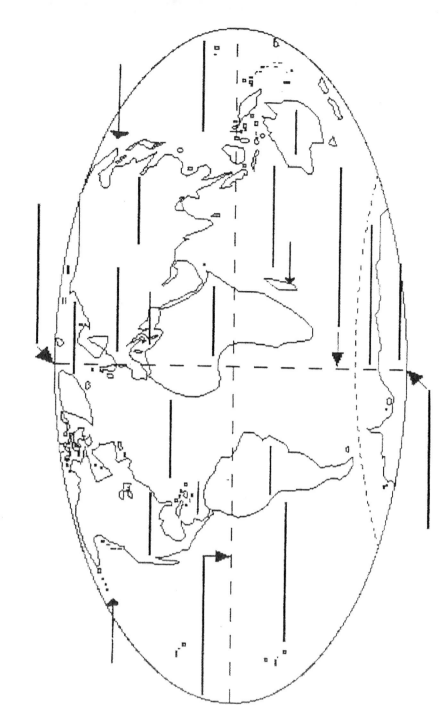

1. Africa
2. Antarctica
3. Arctic Ocean
4. Asia
5. Atlantic Ocean
6. Australia
7. Bering Straights
8. Caribbean Sea
9. Equator
10. Europe
11. Indian Ocean
12. Madagascar
13. Mediterranean Sea
14. North America
15. North Pole
16. Pacific Ocean
17. Prime Meridian
18. South America
19. South Pole
20. Southern Ocean

Map Quiz #2 - At the direction of your instructor, complete one or more of the following exercise options. USE MAP ON FOLLOWING PAGE.

Option A: Using colored pens or highlighters, outline or highlight one country in Africa one in Asia on the following map where apes currently live in the wild. Include: Chimpanzees, Bonobos, Gorillas (mountain and lowland), Orang Utans, Gibbons, and Siamangs.

Option B: Using colored pens or highlighters, outline or highlight one country in Africa or Asia where prosimians (Primates know commonly as the Tarsier, Lemur, and Loris) currently live in the wild.

Option C: Locate the following countries, features and zones on the following map. You may be asked to turn this in as an exercise or locate these from memory as a class quiz.

1. The "New World"
2. The "Old World"
3. United States
4. Mexico
5. Costa Rica
6. India
7. China
8. Siberia
9. Japan
10. Korea
11. Java
12. Mongolia
13. Vietnam
14. The Himalayas
15. Tanzania

16. Ethiopia
17. Kenya
18. Rwanda
19. Nile River
20. Democratic Republic of the Congo
21. Sahara Desert
22. Andes Mountains
23. Amazon Basin
24. Tierra del Fuego
25. Straights of Gibraltar
26. Spain
27. France
28. Germany
29. England
30. Russia

101

World Map.

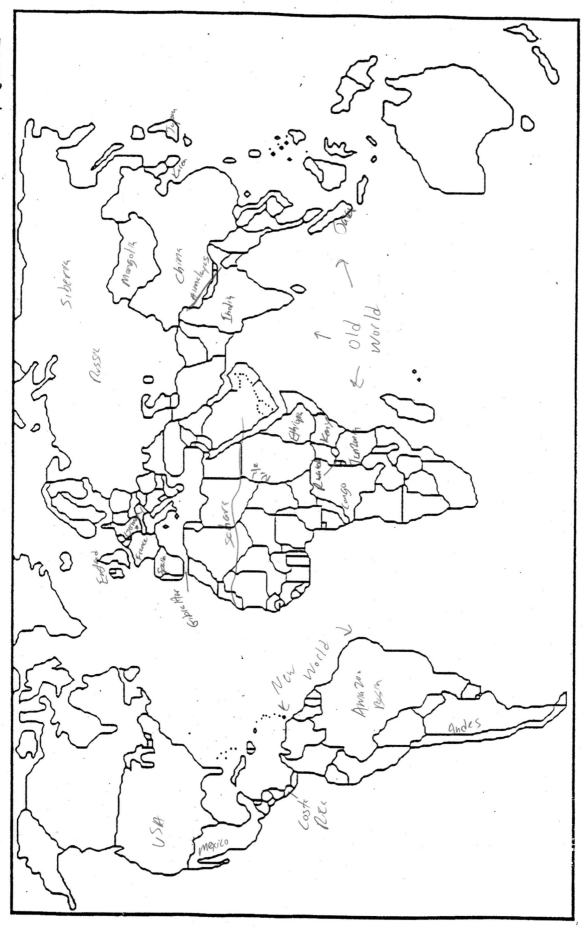

You may find it useful to make extra copies of this blank map for use in future study activities.

Map Quiz #3: Primate Studies, Fossils & Sites. At the direction of your instructor, complete the following as an exercise or use it to study for an in-class quiz.

Find and name the countries where these living primates, fossils, or sites are located

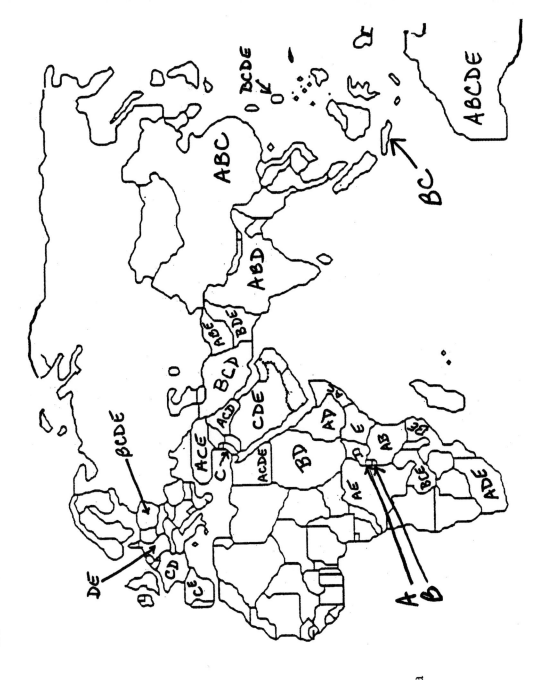

1. Mountain Gorillas studied by Dian Fossey (Karisoke Reserve.)
2. Chimpanzees studied by Jane Goodall (Gombe Reserve.)
3. Taung Child
4. Zinj
5. Lucy
6. Laetoli Footprints
7. ER1470
8. Java Man
9. Peking Man
10. Turkana Boy
11. Torralba and Ambrona
12. Shanidar
13. Old Man of the Chapel of the Saints.
14. Skhul V
15. Neander Valley
16. Cro-Magnon
17. Sima de los Huesos
18. Lazcaux
19. Klasies River Mouth
20. Lake Mungo and/or Malakunanja

Exercise #1: Building Fundamental Vocabulary

Look up the following and prepare a written definition for your class notes. Use these in sentence that is appropriate for the subject matter of this class. Your instructor may assign this as an exercise or as preparation for an in-class quiz.

Prefixes and suffixes:

1. anthro-
2. bio-
3. geo-
4. paleo-
5. prima
6. osteo-
7. –ology
8. homo-
9. hetero-

Subfields of anthropology:

10. Cultural anthropology
11. Archaeology
12. Linguistics
13. Biological or Physical anthropology

Other useful fields or terms:

14. Palynology
15. Forensic anthropology
16. Ecological
17. Environmental
18. Habitat
19. Hominid
20. Human
21. Race
22. Culture
23. Adaptive radiation
24. Gradualism
25. Punctuated equilibrium
26. Natural selection.

You or your instructor may wish to add other useful terms below:

_____
_____
_____
_____
_____
_____
_____
_____
_____
_____
_____
_____
_____
_____
_____
_____
_____
_____
_____
_____
_____
_____
_____
_____
_____
_____
_____
_____

Exercise #2: Animal Taxonomy

Provide the taxonomic names for each of these familiar life forms. Using a blank piece of paper, see if you can reshape these terms into a "family tree" with appropriate branches.

CLASSIFICATION	HUMAN	CHIMPANZEE	GORILLA
KINGDOM			
PHYLUM			
CLASS			
ORDER			
SUBORDER			
SUPERFAMILY			
FAMILY			
GENUS			
SPECIES			

Exercise #3: Seeing Primate Taxonomy

(a) From the Internet or other printed sources, find and print/copy one small image of each of the primates listed in the 14 numbered examples in *italics* below. (b) Arrange these images in a primate family tree, provide the full genus and species name for each image and attach to this cover. This will help you identify primates you see in class film. Your instructor may ask that you turn this in as homework.

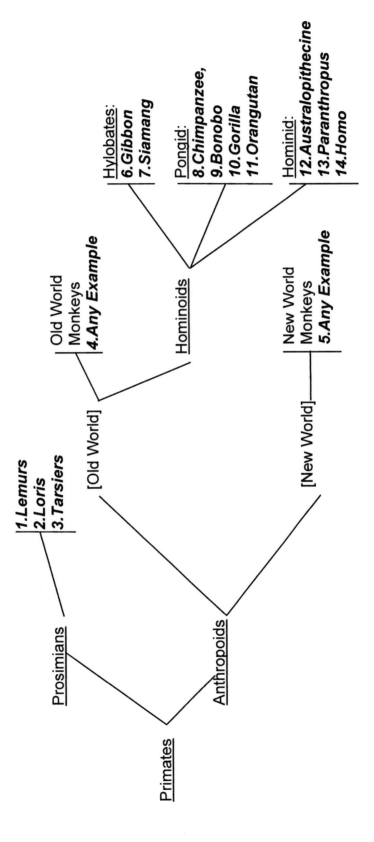

Prosimians
1.*Lemurs*
2.*Loris*
3.*Tarsiers*

[Old World]

Old World
Monkeys
4.*Any Example*

Hominoids

Hylobates:
6.*Gibbon*
7.*Siamang*

Pongid:
8.*Chimpanzee,*
9.*Bonobo*
10.*Gorilla*
11.*Orangutan*

Hominid:
12.*Australopithecine*
13.*Paranthropus*
14.*Homo*

Primates

Anthropoids

[New World]

New World
Monkeys
5.*Any Example*

Exercise #4. The Skeleton. Using the images on the following page, locate these skeletal parts. You may be asked to turn this in as an exercise or locate these from memory as a class quiz.

Vertebral Column:

1. Cervical
2. Thoracic
3. Lumbar
4. Sacrum
5. Coccyx

Upper Torso

6. Clavicle
7. Scapula
8. Sternum

Upper Limbs

9. Humerus
10. Ulna
11. Radius
12. Carpals
13. Metacarpals
14. Phalanges

Pelvis

15. Ilium
16. Ischium
17. Pubis

Lower Limbs

18. Femur
19. Patella
20. Tibia
21. Fibula
22. Tarsals
23. Metatarsals
24. Phalanges

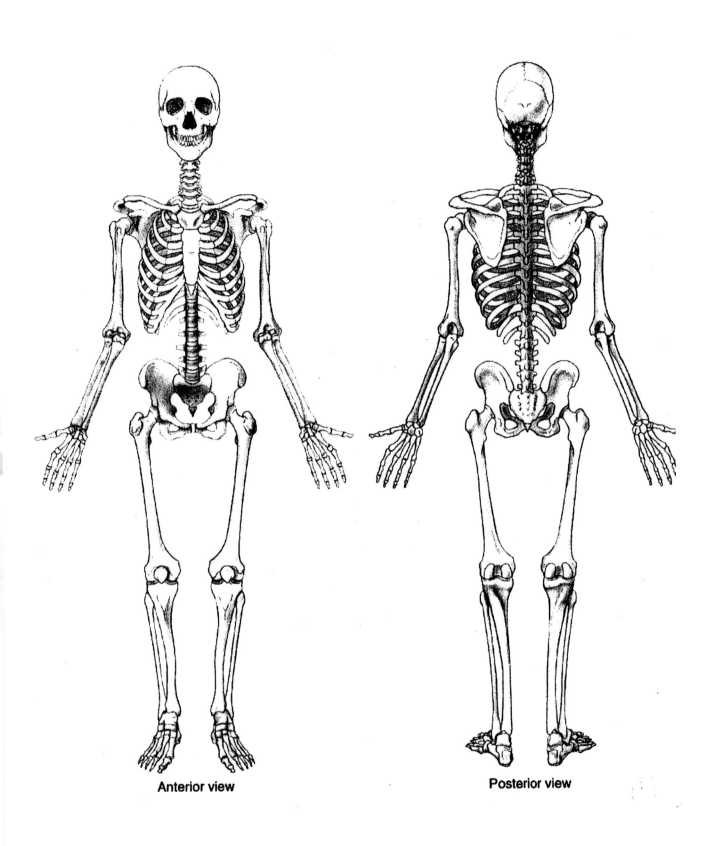

Anterior view

Posterior view

115

Exercise #5: The Skull. At the direction of your instructor, label these significant skull parts as an exercise or use this page to prepare for an in-class quiz.

1. Parietal
2. Occipital
3. Temporal
4. Mandible

5. Maxilla
6. Nasal bone
7. Zygomatic Arch
8. Foramen Magnum

9. Incisors
10. Canine
11. Pre-molars
12. Molars

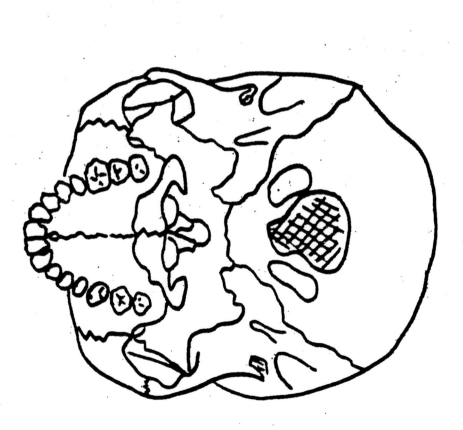

Name_____

Exercise #6: Primate Study Chart #1 – Prosimians & Monkeys

Selected Primate Forms	Geographical Area(s)	Habitat Notes*
PROSIMIANS		
Lemur		
Loris		
Tarsier		
ANTHROPOIDS		
New World Monkey (examples)		
Marmoset		
Howler		
Old World Monkey (examples)		
Macaque		
Baboon		
Other		

*HABITAT CODE: Use these letters to record, review, or practice what you know about primates. There may be several variations within these animal names. Your instructor will guide you in being either general or specific about descriptions.

I=Insectivores   **A**=Arboreal   **N**=Nocturnal   **Sol**=Solitary

V=Vegetarian   **T**=Terrestrial   **D**=Diurnal   **MN**=Monogamous

M=Some meat   **F**=Forest/Semi Forest   **Tr** ="Troup" Social Groups

O=Omnivore   **S**=Savannah   **Fm**="Family" Social Groups

R=Reduced population numbers   **E**=Endangered/possible extinction in our lifetime.

Exercise #7 - Primate Study Chart #2 -- The Apes

Selected Primate Forms	Geographical Area(s)	Habitat Notes*
ANTHROPOIDS, cont.		
Apes		
Hylobates Gibbon/Siamang		
Pongids Orangutan		
Gorilla- (Mountain)		
Gorilla- (Lowland)		
Chimpanzee- Common		
Chimpanzee- Bonobo		

*HABITAT CODE: Use these letters to record, review, or practice what you know about primates. There may be several variations within these animal names. Your instructor will guide you in being either general or specific about descriptions.

I=Insectivores A=Arboreal N=Nocturnal Sol=Solitary
V=Vegetarian T=Terrestrial D=Diurnal MN=Monogamous
M=Some meat F=Forest/Semi Forest Tr ="Troup" Social Groups
O=Omnivore S=Savannah Fm="Family" Social Groups
R=Reduced population numbers E=Endangered/possible extinction in our lifetime.

Exercise #8: Fossil Populations Study Chart #1* - Early hominids

Genus	Common species names?	Examples by fossil name or site?	Average cranial capacity? Cranial range?	Range of dates on earth?	Location of important sites?	Nature of habitat or climate?
Australopithecus	Afarensis Africanus Robustus Boisei anamensis	Lucy Taung Child	410 - 530	4.2 - 1 mya	Lucy - Ethiopia Taung - South Africa	
Paranthropus	Robustus Boisei aethiopicus	SK 47 OH 5		1.5 - 2 mya robustus/boisei 2.3 - 1 mya	Swartskrans, SA Tanzania	

*You may be asked to turn this in as an exercise or provide this data from memory as a classroom exam

Exercise #9: Fossil Populations Study Chart #2*- Early Homo

Genus species	Other related species names?	Examples by fossil name or site?	Average cranial capacity? Cranial range?	Range of dates on earth?	Location of important sites?	Nature of habitat or climate?
Homo habilis	rudolfensis	KNM-ER1470	631	2.5 - 1.5 mya	Kubi Fora, East Turkana	
Homo erectus	ergaster	KNM-ER3733 KNM-wt 15000	750 - 1250cc +900 cc	~~hannoon~~ 1.8mya - 100,000		

*You may be asked to turn this in as an exercise or provide this data from memory as a classroom exam

Exercise #10: Fossil Populations Study Chart #3* - Archaic and modern sapiens

Genus species	Other related species names?	Examples by fossil name or site?	Average cranial capacity? Cranial range?	Range of dates on earth?	Location of important sites?	Nature of habitat or climate?
Archaic Homo sapiens	heidelbergensis	Bodo Ethiopia	600 - 130 Kya	600 - 130 Kya		
Anatomically modern Homo sapiens						

*You may be asked to turn this in as an exercise or provide this data from memory as a classroom exam

Exercise #11: Your environmental footprint?

Go to the following website and take the quiz you find there.

http://www.myfootprint.org

The impact of US and European lifestyles on our collective global environment and resources are different from the impact of most other countries around the world. The Internet provides many comparisons for further study.

What are the major environmental issues you see needing our attention beyond those apparent in the "myfootprint" exercise? List them here with any ideas you may have see for addressing them:

Does humankind face extinction or further evolution? Will it be cultural or biological evolution, or both? Which transformations lie ahead for hominids? For you?

Acknowledgements

From FRAUD'S, MYTHS, AND MYSTERIES, "Epistemology: How You Know What You Know" by Kenneth L. Feder. Copyright © The McGraw-Hill Companies. Reprinted with permission.

From DISCOVER MAGAZINE, "Dr. Darwin," by Lori Oliwenstein. Copyright © 1995 by Lori Oliwenstein. Reproduced with permission of Lori Oliwenstein and Discover Syndication.

"Bittersweet Harvest: The Debate Over Genetically Modified Crops" by Honor Hsin. Copyright © Spring 2002 Harvard International Review. Reprinted with permission.

"Black, White, Other" by Jonathan Marks. Reprinted from NATURAL HISTORY December 1994; Copyright © Natural History Magazine Inc. Reprinted with permission.

"The Evolution of Human Birth" by Karen R. Rosenberg and Wenda R. Trevathan. Reprinted with permission. Copyright © 2001 by Scientific American, Inc. All rights reserved.

From GORILLAS IN THE MIST by Dian Fossey. Copyright © 1983 by Dian Fossey. Reproduced by Houghton Mifflin Company. All rights reserved.

From IN THE SHADOW OF MAN by Jane Goodall. Copyright © 1971 by Hugo and Jane van Lawick-Goodall. Reproduced by permission of Houghton Mifflin Company. All rights reserved.

From DISCOVER MAGAZINE, "Are we in Anthropodenial?" by Frans de Waal. Copyright © 1997 by Frans de Waal. Reproduced with permission of Frans de Waal and Discover Syndication.

From FOREIGN AFFAIRS, "A Natural History of Peace" by Robert M. Sapolsky. Copyright © 2006 by the Council on Foreign Relations, Inc. Reprinted with permission.

"Lucy Kind Takes Humanlike Turn" by Joel Greenberg. SCIENCE NEWS BY GREENBERG, JOEL. Copyright © 2003 by SCI SERVICE INC. Reproduced with permission of SCI SERVICE INC in the format Textbook via Copyright Clearance Center.

"First Family's Last Stand" by Bruce Bower. SCIENCE NEWS BY B.BOWER. Copyright © 2003 by SCI SERVICE INC. Reproduced with permission of SCI SERVICE INC in the format Textbook via Copyright Clearance Center.

"Unified Erectus: Fossil Suggests Single Human Ancestor" by J. Pickrell. Copyright © 2002 by SCI SERVICE INC. Reproduced with permission of SCI SERVICE INC in the format Textbook via Copyright Clearance Center.

"Ancestral Split in China" by Bruce Bower. SCIENCE NEWS BY B.BOWER. Copyright © 2003 by SCI SERVICE INC. Reproduced with permission of SCI SERVICE INC in the format Textbook via Copyright Clearance Center.

"Gene Test Probes Neandertal Origins" by Bruce Bower. SCIENCE NEWS BY B.BOWER. Copyright © 2000 by SCI SERVICE INC. Reproduced with permission of SCI SERVICE INC in the format Textbook via Copyright Clearance Center.